Zack

A Comedy

Harold Brighouse

A SAMUEL FRENCH ACTING EDITION

FOUNDED 1830

SAMUELFRENCH-LONDON.CO.UK
SAMUELFRENCH.COM

FOR AMATEUR PRODUCTION ENQUIRIES

UNITED KINGDOM AND WORLD EXCLUDING NORTH AMERICA

plays@SamuelFrench-London.co.uk

020 7255 4302/01

Each title is subject to availability from Samuel French,

depending upon country of performance.

ZACK

Paul Munning

Zachariah Munning

Joe Wrigley

James Abbott

Thomas Mowatt

Harry Shoebridge

Mrs Munning

Virginia Cavender

Martha W rigley

Sally Teale

ACT I   Mrs Munning's Parlour. An afternoon in
early June

ACT II   The Refreshment Room. Morning, a fortnight
later

ACT III   Mrs Munning's Parlour. Evening, a month
later

The action takes place in the village of Little Hulton,
Lancashire

ACT I

The parlour in Mrs. Munning's *house, the window of which looks out to a bowling green. The room is furnished with chairs and sofa, upholstered in horsehair. It is not quite shabby, but well used. The ornaments crowded on the mantelpiece are Mid-Victorian survivals. There is a bookshelf on the wall above the bureau. The wall-paper is flowered ; there is no gas, but lamp on table. In the window is a small model in plaster of a wedding-cake. It should be quite small and unostentatious. Men's coats are hung behind door. The light is of a spring afternoon.*

As the curtain rises, Mrs. Munning, *who is fifty-five and hard featured, is dusting the ornaments on the mantel. She is in her best clothes, which are black, protected by a dirty apron. She looks at the clock impatiently. It strikes four. She goes to window and looks out. She mutters, " And time too," and goes to door. She opens it and speaks through it.*

Mrs Munning. Get a move on, now. Take your things off in there and come along quick.

Sally (*off*). Yes, Mrs. Munning.

Mrs. Munning. Hurry up when I tell you. This is a nice time of day to come.

Sally (*entering, a pretty, country girl of eighteen in print frock*). You told me to come o' Thursday and Thursday 'tis.

MRS. MUNNING. It's been Thursday a long time.

SALLY. You never said no hour. And mother said to me, she says——

MRS. MUNNING. Never mind what she said. You take hold of that duster and let me see you shape.

SALLY. Yes, Mrs. Munning. (*She takes it and dusts at mantel.*)

MRS. MUNNING. Take care of those ornaments now, Sally.

SALLY. Now don't you fret yourself. I'm not the breaking sort. You can stop my wages for all I'm like to break.

MRS. MUNNING. That's of course.

SALLY. I was telling you. Mother, she says to me, you stay at home for your dinner, she says, and that'll save Mrs. Munning a bit; and I stayed willing because we'd trotters to-day and they're a dish that I've a relish for.

MRS. MUNNING. You could have gone home to your dinner.

SALLY. And I couldn't. Not when I'd once begun with you. Meals and all, you said, and a bargain's a bargain.

MRS. MUNNING. Well, you should have come this morning. Leaving me all to do.

SALLY. Mother didn't know you were in a hurry.

MRS. MUNNING. She ought to, then. I told her. I told her that when Miss Cavender came this afternoon I wanted her to take you for a regular maid. And don't you forget it neither, Sally, and go giving it away you're not always here.

SALLY. Suppose she asks me, Mrs. Munning?

MRS. MUNNING. If you'll shape properly, she'll never think but what you're regular. That's what I wanted you early for. To run you round and show you the ways of the house.

SALLY. Eh, but I don't need showing. Didn't I spring-clean for you last year ? I'll manage easy.

MRS. MUNNING. You'll have to now. And don't come asking me where things are kept, not when Miss Cavender can hear you ask.

SALLY. Oh, don't you worry, Mrs. Munning. If any one gives it away to Miss Cavender that I've not been here for years and years, it'll not be me. Find my way about a strange house blindfold, I can. It's a natural gift.

(PAUL MUNNING *enters, a man of thirty, well-built, but with meanness stamped upon an otherwise not unattractive face. He wears light clothes with a grey bowler hat, and a button-hole.*)

SALLY. Here's Mr. Paul. Good-afternoon, sir.

(PAUL *grunts.* MRS. MUNNING *turns.*)

PAUL. Has she come yet ?
MRS. MUNNING. Not yet. Have you—— ?

(PAUL *indicates* SALLY.)

Um. This room will do now, Sally.

SALLY. It will, though I says it that did it.

MRS. MUNNING. Did you ! I fancied I did it myself.

SALLY. You did the rough, Mrs. Munning, but I always say it's the finishing touch that counts with dusting and I reckon I did that.

MRS. MUNNING. Well, now you can go to the kitchen and get the kettle on for tea.

SALLY. You'll be having your tea in here, won't you ?

MRS. MUNNING. Yes.

SALLY. All right. You needn't raise a hand to it. I'll see to everything.

(SALLY *goes out.*)

MRS. MUNNING. She's a Miss Know-all, she is.

PAUL. Won't she do ?

MRS. MUNNING. She'll have to do. Virginia's got to think we keep a maid, and Sally's the only one who'd come at our price.

PAUL (*sitting, gloomily*). It's great expense.

MRS. MUNNING. No helping that. It's got to be. We can't have Virginia going home and telling all her aunt's too poor to keep a servant. Did you get that order ?

PAUL. No.

MRS. MUNNING. Not Taylor's ?

PAUL. Wilson, of Norton Parva, is catering for Mrs. Taylor's wedding.

MRS. MUNNING. You mean to say that Wilson got there first ?

PAUL. He hadn't been.

MRS. MUNNING. Then how's he got the order ?

PAUL. He's going to get it. It's the same old tale. They'd heard our weddings aren't as pleasant as they used to be. Knew we were nearest, but they thought they'd give Wilson a chance. A good ten pounds gone from us there.

MRS. MUNNING. Well, I don't know.

PAUL. And I don't know. If I knew I'd alter it. We're doing things no different from what we always did, and yet it's got about our style's gone off. It's not gone off.

MRS. MUNNING. I'm sure it's not. What do they say ? Do they tell you anything ?

PAUL. Folks with a wedding in their house are too up-lifted to say much. They don't explain. What I make out is we're not so hearty as we used to be.

MRS. MUNNING. Hearty?

PAUL. I've heard it said so. God knows what it means. I'm sure I try to be hearty. It's prejudice, and nothing else.

MRS. MUNNING. And word's passed round against us.

PAUL. Seems so.

MRS. MUNNING. It's very bad, Paul.

PAUL. Bad? Don't I know it's bad? Couldn't be worse if it tried. We'll have the shutters up altogether at this rate. The joinery business doesn't keep us alive, and if the catering goes to ruin, we'll go along with it. That's all.

MRS. MUNNING. That's all, is it? Can't you up and fight it? You're losing heart.

PAUL. Enough to make me, too. You can fight a thing you see, but you can't fight a prejudice. It's like hitting air. I tell you what, mother, this is no time to have a guest, and a guest that calls for a servant.

MRS. MUNNING. We can't afford to lose a chance.

PAUL. Chance of what?

MRS. MUNNING. There's money in that family, and when my sister writes to me and says Virginia's not been well and needs the country air, I say it's folly not to have her here, cost what it may.

PAUL. There's money and they'll keep it to themselves.

MRS. MUNNING. I'm not the one to go expecting much, but you never know, and it 'ud be no more than sisterly of Annie to remember me in her will.

PAUL. Oh well, she's coming and we're in for it. How long before we see the back of her?

MRS. MUNNING. The doctor told her mother it'll take a month to put her right.

PAUL. A month! A month! Good Lord! There's Sally at six shillings a week wages, that's one pound four, and as much again for keep, is two pounds eight, and Virginia an invalid 'll cost——

MRS. MUNNING. She's not an invalid. She's just run down.

PAUL. I know, and the Lord knows what it'll cost in fancy goods to wind her up. You'll see no change from five pounds for this affair.

MRS. MUNNING. I say it's worth it.

PAUL. And I hope you're right.

MRS. MUNNING. We'll see. You'd better change your clothes now, Paul.

PAUL. Change? What for?

MRS. MUNNING. When I married your father I married a joiner and I didn't see cause to tell our Annie that he couldn't make ends meet till I turned to and made a catering business for him as well, me being apprenticed to the confectionery when he came courting me. I didn't tell them and I haven't told to this day.

PAUL. Yes, but if the girl's to stay a month she's bound to know it soon or late.

MRS. MUNNING. Then let her know it late. There's a lot in first impressions.

PAUL. Why, there's Mr. Abbott's wedding-party to-morrow.

MRS. MUNNING. That's not to-day, is it? And we'll send her for a walk to-morrow with Zack, out of the way.

PAUL. About all he's fit for.

MRS. MUNNING. You get your gay clothes changed,

Paul, or she'll ask questions at once. I've tea to see to now. (*Opening door.*) Sally!

SALLY (*appearing with folded cloth*). Now it's all right, Mrs. Munning. I'm finding all I want.

(PAUL *goes out.* SALLY *unfolds and lays on table a ragged white cloth.*)

MRS. MUNNING. What do you call that?

SALLY. Tea-cloth, isn't it?

MRS. MUNNING. Yes, for the kitchen. I've got one here for this room. (*She opens drawer in table and takes out cloth.*)

SALLY (*watching*). Oh! Company cloth, like.

MRS. MUNNING. Take the other back.

(SALLY *is going.*)

And here, Sally.

SALLY (*turning*). Yes, Mrs. Munning.

MRS. MUNNING (*going to window, getting the wedding-cake model*). Take this with you and put it in the dresser drawer.

SALLY. The dresser drawer!

MRS. MUNNING. And mind you close it.

SALLY. Well I—— Oh, I see. You're hiding it.

MRS. MUNNING. We don't want Miss Cavender to be learning everything at once.

SALLY. A nod's as good as a wink to me. I'm mum.

(SALLY *goes out, with model and cloth, nodding sagely.* MRS. MUNNING *carefully spreads the new cloth on table, putting the lamp on the bureau.* SALLY *re-enters with tray, which she places on the table with a flourish.* MRS. MUNNING *surveys the tray.*)

MRS. MUNNING. That'll not do, Sally.

SALLY. What's wrong now ?

MRS. MUNNING. You mustn't bring in the loaf like that. I want cut bread and butter.

SALLY. Oh, well I call that making work, especially with a loaf like that, all over nobbly bits of crust that's twice as sweet to eat for tearing off.

MRS. MUNNING. And that cress ?

SALLY (*bridling*). Well ?

MRS. MUNNING. It's for cress sandwiches.

SALLY. Oh ? I didn't see no ham nor nothink.

MRS. MUNNING. Cress sandwiches, Sally.

SALLY. How can they be sandwiches without there's meat ?

MRS. MUNNING. Can you cut them or must I do it myself ?

SALLY. Can I ? Of course I can. But I call it a finicky way of doing things. Making a nuisance of a simple job like eating cress. What are fingers for ?

MRS. MUNNING. That will do, Sally. I want no grumbling.

(SALLY *takes up loaf and cress.*)

SALLY. Grumbling ? There never was nobody less of a grumbler than me. I only speak my mind.

MRS. MUNNING. Well, you get along and cut that bread up now. I want things looking nice. Lord ! If that isn't the fly now. Quick, Sally ! Put those plates down in yonder and get back to the door. (*She hustles* SALLY *out. By the door she takes off her apron, and pitches it through door.*) Hang that up sometime. Come along, now. Get to the front door.

(SALLY *re-enters.*)

SALLY. It's all right, Mrs. Munning. Don't you get

yourself into a tear. There's another day to-morrow.
(SALLY *crosses to front door and exit.*)

(MRS. MUNNING *becomes very much the·lady of leisure. She
pats her hair, takes a book from shelf and sits in arm-chair,
reading.* SALLY *re-enters with* VIRGINIA, *a well-dressed
girl of the urban type with plenty of high spirits and some
little indication of recent illness.*)

SALLY. The young lady's here.

(SALLY *remains, an interested spectator.*)

MRS. MUNNING (*marking her place in the book, and rising*).
Well, so this is Virginia. How you've grown !

VIRGINIA. How are you, Aunt Elizabeth ?

MRS. MUNNING. I'm strong and hearty, child. It's you
that's not.

VIRGINIA. Oh, I'm all right now, aunt.

MRS. MUNNING. You're pale.

VIRGINIA. But not for long in this air of yours. There
isn't much the matter with me.

MRS. MUNNING. Your mother wrote a different tale from
that.

VIRGINIA. Mother's a dear old fuss.

MRS. MUNNING. How is she ?

VIRGINIA. She's splendid, thanks.

MRS. MUNNING. Well, give Sally your coat and sit down.

VIRGINIA. Thanks.

(SALLY *takes her coat, then stands examining it.*)

MRS. MUNNING. That's right. And now, Virginia——

VIRGINIA. Jenny, please, aunt.

MRS. MUNNING. Jenny !

VIRGINIA. Virginia's no name to live with.

MRS. MUNNING. Well, as you like. Why don't you sit ?

VIRGINIA. I didn't pay the flyman.

MRS. MUNNING. As if we'd let you! It'll be a pleasure to Paul to see to that. You'll remember Paul?

VIRGINIA. Very vaguely. As a tiny boy.

MRS. MUNNING. He's a big man now. He'll be helping the flyman up with your boxes, only we don't hear them because this house is so extraordinarily well-built you can't hear sounds in it at all. It's a perfect refuge of peace. Just what you want to cure your nerves with quiet and——

(*Several loud bumps are heard above.* MRS. MUNNING *looks disconcerted.*)

VIRGINIA (*quickly*). I'm afraid my box is very heavy.

MRS. MUNNING (*recovering*). Oh, Paul won't mind. He's wonderfully strong. Will you have tea now or would you rather go to your room first? Sally shall show you.

VIRGINIA (*rising*). Thank you.

MRS. MUNNING (*speaking at* SALLY). Our guest room is directly over here.

(VIRGINIA *nods and goes out.*)

SALLY. That's your room, Mrs. Munning.

MRS. MUNNING. You keep that to yourself.

(SALLY *nods, and goes out after* VIRGINIA. MRS. MUNNING *fusses a moment at the tea table, then suddenly thinking, goes to the window and opens it.*)

(*Calling softly*). Zack! Zack! Zack!

(PAUL *enters. He has changed to a brown suit of country cut.*)

PAUL. What do you want Zack for? (*He speaks at her back.*)

MRS. MUNNING (*turning violently*). Eh? Oh, it's you.

PAUL. Yes. What's to do ?

MRS. MUNNING. I've had so much on hand with that Sally turning up so late that it slipped my mind about Zack.

PAUL. What about Zack ?

MRS. MUNNING. I've forgotten to warn him.

PAUL. Warn ?

MRS. MUNNING. About the catering, and Sally and so on. If we don't make it as plain to him as Monday's dinner he'll give us away in the inside of two minutes. You know what Zack is.

PAUL. I'd leave him alone. He's safer out of the way than in it.

MRS. MUNNING. That'll not do. He'll chose the best wrong time for turning up. Trust Zack for doing something awkward.

PAUL (*going* L.). I'll have a look round.

MRS. MUNNING. As like as not the wastrel's sleeping somewhere.

PAUL. Or reading in a book.

MRS. MUNNING. I'll give him read.

(*Enter* SALLY).

You've been a fine time showing Miss Cavender her room.

(*Exit* PAUL.)

SALLY. I've been helping her undo her box, Mrs. Munning.

MRS. MUNNING. Trust you for prying, I suppose.

SALLY. I didn't look before she asked me. But when I did, I saw some sights. The ironing she'll make. Frills ! They're the width of my hand and more.

MRS. MUNNING (*angrily*). Will you go into the kitchen and get those sandwiches cut ?

SALLY. I'm going. (*She gets to door, then turns.*) But I'll tell you this much, Mrs. Munning, that there'll be a row of eyes on washing day a-watching me hang Miss Cavender's underlinen on the line. This village hasn't seen such sights before.

MRS. MUNNING. You mind your own business in there and don't waste time. I'll ring for tea. (*She pushes* SALLY *out, then goes to window.*) Can't you find him, Paul ?

PAUL. Not yet. (*He is outside window.*)

MRS. MUNNING. Best leave it, then. If he's asleep he may sleep on till after tea and then we'll tell him quietly.

PAUL. What ! Zack sleep while there's eating going on ?

MRS. MUNNING. We'll have to chance it, Paul. I want you here when she comes down wherever Zack may be. You didn't see her upstairs ?

PAUL. No. Dodged her.

MRS. MUNNING. That's right.

(PAUL *comes from window and enters by door.* MRS. MUNNING *closes window, and then arranges table again, fussily.*)

PAUL (*grumbling*). Tea in here.

MRS. MUNNING. Why, of course.

(PAUL *sits sulkily in arm-chair, legs outstretched, hands in pocket.*)

PAUL. It's a sight more comfortable in the kitchen. This is a foul upset of all our ways.

MRS. MUNNING. Wait till you see Virginia.

PAUL. I don't need seeing her. I carried up her traps and that's enough to tell me all I want to know.

MRS. MUNNING. A girl must have clothes, Paul.

PAUL. I'd rather carry them than pay for them, that's true. A dressed-up, peeked and pampered town girl with a head full of fancies and——

MRS. MUNNING. I'm sure she isn't peeked.

PAUL. Oh? Isn't she ill, or was her mother lying?

MRS. MUNNING. She's been ill and she's getting better now.

PAUL. That's worse. She'll eat us out of house and home Convalescents always eat like elephants.

MRS. MUNNING. I wish you'd think ahead.

PAUL. I do. To the grocer's bills she'll make.

MRS. MUNNING. Well, you think to something a bit more pleasant that'll bring a smile to your face. You've a sour look on you sometimes.

PAUL. Enough to make me sour, too.

MRS. MUNNING. I've told you why she's here. It's not because I love her, nor her mother neither, but there's money at that end of the family and I'm a believer in keeping on the sweet side of rich relations and giving Providence a friendly lead.

PAUL. I can look pleasant all right when I'm being photographed with a wedding-group, but looking pleasant for a month on end ! It'll take some doing, I give you my word.

(VIRGINIA *enters in a light spring frock.* PAUL *rises.*)

MRS. MUNNING. This is Paul, Jenny.

VIRGINIA. I'm very glad to see you, Cousin Paul. It's a long time since we met.

PAUL (*not ungraciously*). I don't remember meeting you at all.

MRS. MUNNING (*up to bureau, from which she gets a large*

old-fashioned portrait album). Don't you ? I'll show you when you met. Sit down, Jenny.

VIRGINIA (*sitting*). Thanks.

MRS. MUNNING (*sitting by her with the album.* PAUL *stands behind*). I've got you both in this album. Taken together.

PAUL. Oh ?

(MRS. MUNNING *finds the photograph.*)

VIRGINIA. Oh yes. Mother has one of that at home.

MRS. MUNNING. It was taken at your house. Look at it, Paul. Weren't you a loving pair ?

PAUL. Is that me ?

MRS. MUNNING. That's you.

VIRGINIA. Don't you look funny ?

PAUL. You a baby and me a little lad. No wonder I'd forgotten it.

MRS. MUNNING. You've both come on a bit since then. Ring the bell for tea, Paul.

(PAUL *looks surprised, then rings.*)

VIRGINIA (*turning over leaves*). Is this Paul, too ?

MRS. MUNNING. Yes. Paul at five. (*Turning*). And there he is at ten, and there at twelve and——

VIRGINIA. Yes. But haven't I another cousin, Aunt Elizabeth ?

MRS. MUNNING. Yes. Yes, but——

PAUL. He makes a bad photograph.

VIRGINIA. Some people do. But they are often all the better in the flesh. Will he be in to tea ?

MRS. MUNNING. Well——

VIRGINIA. Isn't he at home ?

(SALLY *enters with tea, sandwiches, etc.*)

PAUL. Oh yes. But we're very busy in the joiner's shop just now.

(SALLY *stops short and looks at him.*)

MRS. MUNNING. Come along, Sally.

VIRGINIA. Oh, dear ! But of course I'm glad to know your business does so well. I mean I suppose it does if my cousin is too busy to come in to tea.

MRS. MUNNING. We'll send for him. Sally, tell Mr. Zachary to come.

SALLY. Mr. Zachary ?

MRS. MUNNING. Yes.

SALLY. Do you mean Zack ?

MRS MUNNING. Tell Mr. Zachary tea's ready and his cousin's come.

SALLY. But I don't know where he is. He's such a one for getting into holes and corners and——

PAUL. You can find him, can't you ?

SALLY. I can try. And I'll start with his bed, and all. It's ten to one he's lying on it.

MRS. MUNNING. Sally, he's——

SALLY. Are you finding him or am I ? Because if it's me, I'll look in the likeliest place first.

(*Exit* SALLY.)

MRS. MUNNING. You mustn't expect town courtesy from our country servants, Jenny. May I give you sugar ?

VIRGINIA. One lump, please.

MRS. MUNNING. And cream ?

VIRGINIA. Thanks.

MRS. MUNNING. Paul, Jenny's cup.

(PAUL *hands it clumsily. While they are occupied the door*

opens, and ZACK *enters. He is younger than* PAUL, *but neglect makes him look middle-aged. He wears spectacles and a beard and is dressed shabbily with a carpenter's apron on. Under his left arm is the wedding-cake model.*)

ZACK. I knew that was the smell of tea-time, but what are we having it in here for ?

MRS. MUNNING. Zack, don't you see your cousin ?

(MRS. MUNNING *pours tea, etc.* VIRGINIA *rises.*)

ZACK. Why, if I'd not forgotten all about her. I am a careless chap. Do you know, Miss Virginia, I forgot to come in to dinner one day last week.

PAUL. That doesn't often happen.

ZACK. It 'ud better not, neither. Gives you a nasty sinking feel towards tea-time to go without your dinner. Well, how are you, Miss Virginia ? I'm pleased to meet you.

(*Till now* VIRGINIA *has stood slightly embarrassed and amused. He comes forward now, and* VIRGINIA *puts out her hand.*)

MRS. MUNNING. You'll wash your hand before you touch Jenny's.

ZACK. Maybe I ought. I'm not so frequent at the soap as I might be.

VIRGINIA. I think we'll shake hands as you are.

ZACK. Will you ? That's hearty.

(*They shake hands.* VIRGINIA *sits,* ZACK *is about to.*)

But—— Oh, Lord !

VIRGINIA. What is it ?

ZACK (*fingering his coat*). I'm not dressed up for a parlour tea. I—— Eh ?

(PAUL *is taking the model from under* ZACK'S *arm.*)

Oh, yes. Do you know where I found that ?

MRS. MUNNING. Put it down.

ZACK (*up to window with it*). I'll put it in its place. But do you know where I found it ?

MRS. MUNNING. Never mind, Zack. It doesn't matter. (*To* JENNY.) It's only a little window ornament, Jenny.

ZACK (*imperviously*). I found that on the kitchen dresser. Picked it up as I came through.

(SALLY *enters.* MRS. MUNNING'S *feelings get too much for her. She rises to meet* SALLY. PAUL *sees and distracts* VIR-GINIA'S *attention.*)

PAUL.· Will you have more bread and butter, Jenny ?

VIRGINIA. Thank you, Paul.

SALLY. I can't find—— (*Seeing* ZACK.) Oh, there you are !

MRS. MUNNING (*to* SALLY). I told you to put that model in the dresser drawer.

SALLY. And you told me to cut sandwiches and bread and I've one pair of hands and not a hundred. I left it atop till I'd a minute to spare, and if it's not where I left it some one's moved it. It didn't walk.

(*She crosses speaking and exit.* MRS. MUNNING *returns speechlessly to her seat.*)

ZACK. Well, I'll change my coat and chance it.

(*He changes to a slightly less old coat which hangs behind the door.*)

Parlour ways is parlour ways.

VIRGINIA. I do hope you're not going to make a stranger of me, Aunt Elizabeth.

ZACK. And that's no use in here. (*Taking off the apron.*)

PAUL. You'll have to make allowances for Zack, Jenny.

VIRGINIA. Is he a little—— ?

PAUL. We don't let it go beyond the family, of course.

VIRGINIA. I hope I'm one of you.

PAUL. He was born lazy. That's what's the matter.

ZACK (*returning to table, sitting and eating. ZACK can talk and eat at once*). I've done a job of work to-day and chance it. Mended that pig-stye at Ballbrook farm.

PAUL. Did you ? I daresay there was all of ten minutes' work in that.

ZACK. Took me a couple of hour.

MRS. MUNNING. Then I hoped you charged according.

ZACK. I charged a shilling.

MRS. MUNNING. For a couple of hour ! It's worth half a crown.

ZACK. I charged what I thought fair.

MRS. MUNNING. What you—— ! Oh well, it's done now. Where's the shilling ?

ZACK (*feeling*). Oh, it's in my other coat. (*He is about to rise.*)

PAUL. All right. All right. That'll do later.

ZACK. But I can see I've done wrong thing again. It's like this, Miss Virginia, there's some folk born to do right. They can't do the wrong thing if they tried. Like mother and Paul. I'm different. It's just the other way with me. I can't do right.

MRS. MUNNING. You never spoke a truer word.

ZACK. Same time, you know, I have my use. Oh yes, I've got a use.

MRS. MUNNING. I haven't noticed it.

ZACK. I'll tell you then. Suppose a thing goes wrong.

They do sometimes. Very well. It couldn't be Paul and it couldn't be you, because you're born the other way. It's always me. You don't need to look round for some one to put the blame on. You know it's me. And that's a sort of use now, isn't it ?

VIRGINIA. Is it ?

ZACK. Think of the time it saves. I'm always handy to be cussed at. Like a cat, you know. Some folks keep a cat or a dog, and when their feelings get too much to hold, they kick the cat. Well, I'm the cat i.1 this house. (*He speaks entirely without bitterness. It is all accepted fact.*)

PAUL. You sleep like one, but a cat's more use than you. You don't catch mice.

ZACK. I eat more, too. And that's a thing I've tried to master and I can't. You'd be surprised the way I've tried to fight my appetite.

MRS. MUNNING. It's news to me.

ZACK. I own it didn't show. It beat me every time Eating agrees with me. That's where it is. I'm a natural-born eater and I can't go against nature.

MRS. MUNNING. You needn't talk about it.

ZACK. No. But it's like my other ways. It can't be hid. I'm eating now in the parlour as hearty as if it were in the kitchen. And that's not right, is it ?

VIRGINIA. I don't know.

ZACK. Parlour's for eating like you didn't mean it, and only played with food to pass the time. I wish I could pretend with food. But the habit's got too strong a hold on me for that. I'll never be a gentleman.

MRS. MUNNING. That'll do, Zack. Talking about yourself with your mouth full. Jenny's heard quite enough.

PAUL. What would you like to do after tea, Jenny ?

VIRGINIA. Anything you like. I must just write to mother first to tell her I got here all right.

MRS. MUNNING. Of course.

VIRGINIA. What time does the post go ?

MRS. MUNNING. Six o'clock.

VIRGINIA. I'd better write at once. Then I shall be quite at your disposal, cousin.

PAUL. I thought you and mother might go out. The country's looking quite like spring.

ZACK. I've noticed the celandine's in bud.

MRS. MUNNING. Are you too tired for a walk, Jenny ?

VIRGINIA. Not at all.

MRS. MUNNING. Then Paul shall take you. Youth with youth.

PAUL. I'm rather busy at the works.

ZACK. Works ! And busy !

PAUL (*silencing him*). Yes, busy. So if you'll excuse me now——

VIRGINIA. Of course.

ZACK. Well ! that's a oner.

PAUL. I'll just clear off my work as quickly as I can.

(*Exit* PAUL.)

ZACK. That'll not take long. Busy !

MRS. MUNNING. Paul's busy if you're not. Hadn't you better go and help him ?

ZACK. There's no work in to help him at. We've never been so slack.

MRS. MUNNING. It's there if you'll go and look for it, and stop making an exhibition of your laziness to your cousin.

ZACK. I haven't finished my tea.

MRS. MUNNING. Every one else has. It's not our fault

you came in late.   Will you write your letter here, Jenny ?
(*Indicates bureau.*)

VIRGINIA.   I have notepaper upstairs, aunt.

MRS. MUNNING.   And you don't use it in this house.
We can run to a sheet of notepaper, I should hope.   Oh,
I was thinking——   (*She opens the portrait album.*)

VIRGINIA.   Yes ?

MRS. MUNNING.   No, there's a better one than that.   I'll
get it for you.   I thought you might like to send your
mother a photograph of Paul.

VIRGINIA.   I'm sure she'll like to have it, aunt.

MRS. MUNNING.   Yes.   I'll run upstairs and get it you.
I've one up there that's better than any of these.

(*Exit* MRS. MUNNING.)

ZACK.   There's queer things happening here to-day, Miss
Virginia.

VIRGINIA.   Are there ?   Why do you call me *Miss*
Virginia ?

ZACK.   You're not a married woman, are you ?

VIRGINIA.   Of course not.   But I don't call you Mr.
Zachary.

ZACK.   Nor nobody else neither.   Mr. Zachary !   I'd
not know who you meant.

VIRGINIA.   Why don't you call me Jenny, like the others
do ?

ZACK.   I'm not same as the others, you see.

VIRGINIA.   You're my cousin just as much as Paul is.

ZACK.   I suppose that's true.   There's funny things in
nature, too.   By gum, there are.   To think of the likes of
me being own cousin to the likes of you.

VIRGINIA.   So you'll call me Jenny.

ZACK. I'd *like* to, if you think it's quite respectful.

VIRGINIA. Bother respect. I'm Jenny and you're Zack, and that's settled.

ZACK. Well, I never thought—eh, but we're getting on champion, Jenny. I'm still a bit worried in my mind, though.

VIRGINIA. Not about my name ?

ZACK. Oh no. Settled's settled. It's, well—this for a start. (*He takes up the model.*) What did mother want to hide it away for ?

VIRGINIA. What is it, Zack ?

ZACK (*holding it towards her*). You can see what it is.

VIRGINIA. A wedding cake ?

ZACK. Aye, but you wouldn't thank me for a slice of this. It's plaster. How are folks to know we are caterers unless they can see that in the window ? It's like keeping a pub and putting your sign away.

VIRGINIA. But I thought you were joiners.

ZACK. We crack to be because joinery was father's trade. But it's mother's trade we mostly live by. She's a masterpiece at cooking, only the business isn't thriving. Wedding spreads are the best part of it. Folk are a bit slow at getting wed, some road.

VIRGINIA. I don't think aunt wanted me to know about this, Zack.

ZACK. She's no cause to hide it, then. Father was a bit like me, not much inclined to work, and I reckon I'm proud of my mother for working for two. But things aren't what they were. Folks won't spend like they used to. They buy furniture instead of feasting so much. And our weddings have a bad name, too. I don't know how it is. I'm sure Paul tries.

VIRGINIA. And do you go to them ?

ZACK. Not now, with things so bad. I used to go until my clothes wore out—well, they weren't mine at all properly speaking. They were father's when he was alive and then I had them, but I'm hard on clothes somehow. I'm a great expense all ways there are, with being a big eater and all. And when my dress coat gave out at the seams and got that shiny you could see your face in it, mother wouldn't buy me another, and so I don't go now. It's been a sorrow to me, too. I used to take a lot of pleasure in seeing others enjoy themselves. But I wasn't any use, not real use, like Paul. I couldn't boss things like he does. I just was there and tried to tell the old maids that their day would come. But I couldn't even do my fair share of waiting because of a weakness that I have.

VIRGINIA. A weakness ! Zack, it isn't——

ZACK. Oh, no. Not that. I'm a teetotaller, Jenny. I get that worked up with the hearty feeling of it that I break the plates. My hand's unsteady. (*Takes plates from table.*) See ! That's steady enough ? Yes, but get me waiting at a table full of wedding guests and it seems I've got to break the plates to show my pleasure. And it's not wilful. It's not indeed. It's just anxiety to do things right that makes me do them wrong. Mother's quite right. I'm not a bit of good, but I do miss the outings all the same.

VIRGINIA. Poor Zack. I really must get to my letter now, and I think I'll go upstairs after all.

ZACK. I'm not driving you away ?

VIRGINIA. Of course you're not.

(MRS. MUNNING *enters* R.)

MRS. MUNNING. I'm sorry I've been so long, Jenny,
I couldn't lay my hands on the one I wanted. There it is.
(*Giving photograph.*)

VIRGINIA. Oh! It's very good of him.

MRS. MUNNING. I think your mother will be glad to see
it.

VIRGINIA. Yes. (*She isn't interested, and puts the photo-graph on the table.*) I was just going upstairs to write. It
will be quieter in my room.

MRS. MUNNING. Has Zack been talking to you?

ZACK. I did a bit.

MRS. MUNNING. Oh, then I'm not surprised you want
some quiet for a change.

VIRGINIA. I thought I'd not be interrupted there. I
won't be long. (*Going.*)

MRS. MUNNING. You're forgetting the photograph.

VIRGINIA. I'm sorry, aunt. I was thinking of the other
things I had to say to mother. (*She glances at ZACK and
goes out.*)

MRS. MUNNING (*reflectively, looking after her*). I'd give
something to know what she's saying about our Paul in
that letter. (*She turns.*) Why isn't the table cleared?
Couldn't you stir yourself to ring the bell for Sally?

ZACK. I didn't know I ought. A servant girl's a novelty
to me.

MRS. MUNNING. You didn't let that out to Jenny?

ZACK. Let what out?

MRS. MUNNING. Why, that Sally isn't always here.

ZACK. I don't remember that we mentioned her at all.
Aren't we to let that out?

MRS. MUNNING. Of course we're not, you moon-struck
natural! What do you think she's here for?

ZACK. Well, I dunno. Unless she's here to do the work that Jenny makes.

MRS. MUNNING. Work! I'd do all Jenny makes with one hand tied behind me. Sally's here for show, but I'll watch she does some work as well. And I've a word to say to her about that model there. And you as well.

ZACK. Yes, mother.

MRS. MUNNING. I'll see her first. You can wait. Your time's worth nothing and I'm paying her for hers. Now don't you dare to stir from here till I come back.

ZACK. No, mother.

(*Exit* MRS. MUNNING. ZACK *stands stock-still for a minute, then his eye catches the last piece of bread and butter. Tempted, he falls and gets it. Then tiptoes to a chair, takes one large bite out of the slice, gets sleepy, half raises the slice for another bite, lets his hand drop and settles as if to sleep. A knock at the door.* ZACK *half-hears, but decides not to move. The knock repeated. This time he does not hear at all.* MARTHA WRIGLEY *opens the door, and puts a timid head round it. She enters shyly, half child, half woman of eighteen, slovenly and down at heel. She carries a dress suit over her arm. She sees* ZACK *and stops.*)

MARTHA. Oh! Zack!

ZACK. Eh? (*He rouses slowly, not as if from sleep, but from sloth.*) Who's there?

MARTHA. It's Martha Wrigley. And if you please I knocked, and knocked, and nobody came and so——

ZACK (*stirring lazily in his chair*). Just when I had a moment for a bit of rest.

MARTHA. I'm sorry, Zack. I am sorry. Only I had to make somebody hear.

ZACK (*noticing the bread in his hand, and finishing it*). It needn't have been me. I can't tell you anything.

MARTHA (*matter of fact, without malice*). No. I know you're nobody here. But you can tell them that are somebody.

ZACK. Tell 'em what?

MARTHA. Oh, Zack, we're in such trouble at home.

ZACK (*sitting up straight with ready sympathy*). What's to do, Martha?

MARTHA. I don't know what Mrs. Munning will say. It's my father, Zack.

ZACK. What's he done?

MARTHA. He's fallen down and broke his arm and he won't be able to wait at the wedding to-morrow.

ZACK. Joe Wrigley's broke his arm! Well, there's carelessness for you.

MARTHA. Yes. Please, he knows it's careless of him and he'll lose the half-a-crown he gets from you for waiting, and we did need that half-crown so bad.

ZACK (*rising*). You'd better see my mother, Martha.

MARTHA. Couldn't you tell her, Zack. She'll be so mad.

ZACK (*shaking head*). It's not a job I'm pining for.

MARTHA. We've done our best. I've brought my father's suit for some one else to wear. And Zack—— (*She puts the clothes on a chair.*)

ZACK. Nay. This is getting too much for me. I'll fetch my mother.

MARTHA. Yes, but Zack——

ZACK. Well?

MARTHA. We did so hope that Mrs. Munning would see her way to paying father all the same.

ZACK. Paying him when he's not there!

MARTHA. He would be if he could. We do need his money that bad.

ZACK. You'll not get owt from mother. Nothing for nothing's her way of seeing things.

MARTHA. There's been so little lately with you having so few parties.

ZACK. You'll get none out of mother. That's a certain fact.

MARTHA (*blubbering*). And I was so looking forward to a bite of meat. We've not seen butcher's meat at our house not for a month and more.

ZACK (*really hit where he's soft*). My word, that's bad, Martha.

MARTHA. And me anæmic too, and never can get food enough to satisfy me.

ZACK. Not food enough !

MARTHA. I'm always hungry, and this did look a chance of getting my teeth into a bit of meat at last.

ZACK. Well, I dunno. That's very bad. (*He looks at coat behind door.*)

MARTHA. You try it and you'd know.

ZACK. Look here, Martha. This'll get me into trouble, but I got a shilling to-day at Ballbrook Farm, and if it's any use to you well—dang it, mother can't kill me. Here it is—— (*He goes to coat, gets shilling, and brings it to her.*)

(*She takes it and expresses thanks, mostly by crying on his shoulder.*)

MARTHA. Oh, Mr. Zack. You are the good one.

ZACK. There ! There ! There ! There ! There ! Don't take on so.

MARTHA. Oh !

(*She kisses him.* MRS. MUNNING *enters.*)

MRS. MUNNING (*grimly sarcastic*). Oh ? When's the wedding, Zack ?

ZACK (*humouring her*). Oh, I dunno. In about a month, eh, Martha ?

MRS. MUNNING. You're fool enough for anything.

ZACK (*seriously*). I was only consoling her a bit.

MRS. MUNNING. If you want to console young women with your arm around their waists, my lad, you'll not be long for this house. You've enough bad habits now without beginning new ones.

ZACK. Martha was a bit upset, mother.

MRS. MUNNING. It 'ud be a bad case that called for you to set it right. What is it, Martha ?

MARTHA. Father's broke his arm and he can't wait to-morrow, and I've brought his clothes, and, please Mrs. Munning, he's very sorry.

MRS. MUNNING. Sorry ! Here ! Paul ! Paul ! (*Opens door.*) Paul !

PAUL (*off*). Coming.

MRS. MUNNING. And you consoled her for a thing like that ! Console ! I'd use a stick and——

(PAUL *enters.*)

PAUL. What is it, mother ?

MRS. MUNNING. A nice upset, that's what it is. Joe Wrigley's gone and broke his arm when we wanted him to-morrow.

PAUL (*savagely*). The meddling fool ! Disturbing our arrangements. How dare he break his arm ?

MARTHA. Please, Mr. Paul, he didn't mean to. It was an accident.

PAUL. Accident! Didn't he know it was Mr. Abbott's wedding to-morrow?

MARTHA. Yes, sir.

PAUL. Then he shouldn't have an accident. You go and tell your father he's engaged by me to-morrow and if he doesn't come and do his job, he'll get no more work from us. You understand?

MARTHA. But father can't wait to-morrow with a broken arm.

PAUL. That's not my fault. I didn't break it. You tell him what I said.

MARTHA (turning, then). Then you won't be paying him his money, sir?

PAUL. What!

MRS. MUNNING. Paying him! I like your impudence.

ZACK. You'd better go home, Martha.

MARTHA. Yes, Mr. Zack (Crying.) But I am so——

ZACK (his arm about her). There! There! (Leading her towards door.)

MRS. MUNNING. Keep your hands off the girl, Zack.

ZACK. I was only consoling her a bit. (He opens R. door.)

MRS. MUNNING. Then don't do it.

ZACK. No, mother.

(Exit MARTHA.)

MRS. MUNNING. This is a pretty how do you do.

PAUL. Confound Joe Wrigley. I don't know where to get another man at such short notice.

MRS. MUNNING. And labour scarce, and all. Can you manage it with a man short?

(ZACK shyly approaches the clothes on chair and, not lifting them, fingers them lovingly.)

PAUL. No, I can't.

MRS. MUNNING. You'll have to get somebody to-night, then. That's all.

PAUL. If I can. It's going to take some doing to find a steady man.

ZACK. Paul !

PAUL. What's the matter ?

ZACK. Could I go ?

PAUL. You !

ZACK. I'd dearly love to.

PAUL. You're no use.

ZACK. I know my hands are awkward, but I will try, Paul. I'll try so hard not to break anything.

MRS. MUNNING. He'd be better than nothing, Paul.

PAUL. I doubt it.

ZACK. Give me another chance.

PAUL. I gave you chance on chance. You're more trouble than you're worth.

ZACK. I'm not worth anything, and nobody knows it more than me. But couldn't I go this once, just to fill up ? I'll be so careful, Paul.

MRS. MUNNING. It's saving a man's wages for the day.

PAUL. It's not a saving if he makes a mess of things. Our catering's got bad name enough without our making bad to worse. He's got no proper clothes.

ZACK. I'll wear Joe Wrigley's willing. (*He goes to them.*)

PAUL. Joe Wrigley's a big man.

ZACK. Can I try them, Paul ? Do let me try them on.

PAUL. Well, you can try, and show us what sort of a lout you look.

ZACK. Oh, hurrah ! (*He jerks his coat off and fastens on the clothes.*)

Mrs. Munning. It's the best road out, Paul.

Paul. A rotten best.

Zack (*putting on the dress coat. It is far too large for him*). It will be splendid to be wearing black again.

Paul. It's only for to-morrow, mind.

(Paul *does not yet turn to look at* Zack.)

Mrs. Munning. Joe Wrigley's out of it six weeks or more.

Paul. Joe Wrigley's finished himself with me. Zack can go to-morrow till I've time to look round.

Zack. Suppose I'm not so bad to-morrow, Paul ?

Paul. Supposing pigs 'ull fly. Let's have a look at you. Good Lord ! Hold the trousers to you and let us know the worst. Now, I ask you——

Mrs. Munning. I can tack the bottoms up, Paul, and the rest is not so bad.

(*Enter* Virginia. *She has a hat on and her letter in her hand.*)

Virginia. I've finished my—— Oh, Zack, you do look funny.

Curtain.

ACT II.

Morning a fortnight later. The SCENE *is the refreshment-
room attached to* MRS. MUNNING'S *house. Walls white-
washed, roof of glass. Long deal table at the lower end of
which* PAUL *sits writing a letter. Ink and a few papers
on the table. In one corner is a quantity of cane-bottomed
chairs. Below them, another table. Centre is a knife-
cleaning machine, which badly needs oil. Knives on table.
At the machine* ZACK *stands in shirt-sleeves and apron. He
is not energetic and turns lazily with many glances towards*
PAUL. *He sees* PAUL *look at him and his efforts increase
for a moment.* PAUL *seals and stamps envelope and crosses
to house door.* ZACK, *left alone, mops his brow and sits.
A low knock at the street door.* ZACK *rises promptly and
opens door with the air of a conspirator.* MARTHA WRIGLEY
is there.

ZACK. You've just come at the right time.

(MARTHA *enters, but stays by door.* ZACK *hurries behind the
chairs and returns with a small newspaper parcel which he
gives* MARTHA.)

MARTHA. Thank you, Zack.

ZACK (*referring to the parcel*). It's a bit mixed-up on account of me putting bits of things into my pocket at table when nobody's watching, but it's all good food, Martha.

MARTHA. I'm sure I'm very grateful to you, Zack.

ZACK. Well, I often get up famished from my meals, and it's a fight to keep from feeling in my pocket, but I'm managing without.

MARTHA. Yes, and I—— Oh, Zack, I'm grateful. I am, really.

ZACK. I know you are.

MARTHA. Yes, but I want you to know I am, and if anything's going to come to you unpleasant, it's not my fault.

ZACK. Unpleasant ?

MARTHA. I'm being driven, Zack. I'd never dream of such a thing myself.

ZACK. What ever is it ?

MARTHA. It's father, Zack.

ZACK. Again ? What's he broke now ?

MARTHA. He's not broke anything, but you know your brother sacked him, and my father says he'll be revenged and——

ZACK. That's a nasty spirit, Martha.

MARTHA. And a nasty thing that Mr. Paul did, and all.

ZACK. I'm not denying that.

MARTHA. And I'd not mind whatever father did to Mr. Paul——

ZACK. Oh, Martha !

MARTHA. I wouldn't. Not for sacking him because he hurt himself. But father's doing it to you and I've to help him to do it, and—oh dear ! (*Her handkerchief comes out.*)

ZACK. Don't cry. No, don't do it, Martha, because if you do, I'll have to console you, and you know what mother said to me the other day. (*He is itching to " console," but restrains himself visibly.*)

MARTHA. But it's——

ZACK. Paul's coming back. Quick, Martha.

MARTHA (*sniffing as she goes*). Oh !

(ZACK *hustles her out* C. *and returns to his cleaning, not so quickly that* PAUL *does not see his return.* PAUL *opens the door and* VIRGINIA *enters.* PAUL *follows her in.*)

VIRGINIA. You do look busy, Zack.

PAUL. He's good at looking it. I'd guarantee he hasn't raised his hand while I've been out of the room.

VIRGINIA (*who is obviously quite fond of* ZACK). Oh, but you must be kind to Zack to-day.

PAUL. Why ? What's to-day ?

VIRGINIA. I knew you didn't know. Do you, Zack ?

ZACK (*up to wall, consulting calendar*). Tuesday.

VIRGINIA. It's your birthday and I hope you'll have a very lucky day.

ZACK. My birthday ! The twentieth of June. So it is.

(PAUL *returns to his correspondence at the table, half occupied, half listening.*)

VIRGINIA. Yes. I was sure you didn't know.

ZACK. How did you know ? Did mother tell you ?

VIRGINIA. No.

ZACK. Who did ?

VIRGINIA (*with mock impressiveness*). The family Bible, Zack ! Your mother lent it me to look at something yesterday, and there I found it. Zachariah Manning, June 20th, 1886. 1886, Zack.

ZACK. Yes.

VIRGINIA. You knew ?

ZACK. Yes. That's the year all right.

VIRGINIA. Then how dare you look forty when you're only twenty-nine ?

ZACK. Do I ?

VIRGINIA. You do, and I'm taking you in hand. Tell me, are your eyes so very bad ?

ZACK. They're weak for reading with.

VIRGINIA. You're not always reading. Why do you wear your glasses when you're not ?

ZACK. It's a trouble to be taking them off and putting them on.

VIRGINIA. So you keep them on all the time and damage your eyes. Come here, Zack. (*She takes them off and gives them him.*) There ! Don't put those on again until you want to read. You look at least five years younger than you did.

ZACK. Do I ?

VIRGINIA. You do. And now about the rest ?

ZACK. What rest ?

VIRGINIA. The other six years that we've got to wipe away. I've got a present for you upstairs to do that.

ZACK. A present !

VIRGINIA. Yes. Don't you usually get presents on your birthday ?

PAUL. What ! Between grown-ups ?

VIRGINIA. Why not ? It's just those little pleasant things that keep life sweet.

ZACK. I used to get a bag of humbugs when I was a tiny lad.

VIRGINIA. Oh, we keep on doing it at home and I shall do it here. Only I want a ha'penny from you first.

ZACK. A ha'penny !

VIRGINIA. My present cuts, and so you'll have to pay me for it to keep bad luck away. Ha'penny, please! (*She holds hand out.*)

ZACK (*rather hurt at having to confess*). I haven't got a ha'penny, Jenny.

VIRGINIA. What, have you spent last Saturday's wages already? It's only Tuesday.

ZACK. I don't get any wages.

PAUL. We've given up trusting Zack with money. He lost a shilling on the day you came.

VIRGINIA. Oh dear, then what's to be done? I know. You give Zack the ha'penny for a birthday present. Then he can give it me.

PAUL. What is your present, Jenny?

VIRGINIA. It's a shaving-set.

PAUL. Zack's no use for shaving. He's never shaved in his life.

VIRGINIA. His beard looks that kind of beard. That's why I want him to begin. Give him the ha'penny, Paul.

PAUL. Oh, it'll not matter. Zack isn't superstitious.

VIRGINIA. But I am. All decent-minded women are. And I won't cut my friendship for Zack.

PAUL. Well, if you insist. (*Taking coins from pocket.*) Oh, no good. I've got no change.

VIRGINIA. You've got a sixpence there. That will do. (*She takes it and hands it* ZACK.) There you are, Zack. Now you give it me and I'll get your present from upstairs.

PAUL. But—Jenny—sixpence!

(MRS. MUNNING *opens door* L. *and enters with* JAMES ABBOTT, *a pleasant gentleman, dressed in good country clothes.*

The little episode is suspended. PAUL *becomes the shopman with a customer.* ZACK *stands away and* VIRGINIA *sits on the pile of wood.*)

MRS. MUNNING. Paul.

PAUL. Good morning, Mr. Abbott.

ABBOTT. Good morning, Munning.

MRS. MUNNING. Mr. Abbott's called to settle his account, Paul.

PAUL. Account! You are prompt, sir. I only sent it out last night.

ABBOTT. Any objections to prompt settlement, Munning ? (*Paying out notes and gold.*)

PAUL. Not at all. I only wish I could find everybody so quick at paying.

(PAUL *writes receipt at table.*)

ABBOTT. It's like this, Munning. When I'm satisfied I believe in showing it, and paying promptly is my way of showing that you've pleased me.

MRS. MUNNING. I'm very glad to hear that, Mr. Abbott.

ABBOTT. And I'm glad too, for I don't mind telling you now it's over that I had my doubts. The last once or twice that I've attended weddings where you did the catering I've not been well impressed at all. There's been a harshness, Munning, and when I got married I was in two minds about putting it with you or going to those people over at Norton Parva. Wilson's, isn't it ?

PAUL. Yes.

(PAUL *comes out with receipt, which* ABBOTT *takes and pockets.*)

ABBOTT. But I decided to support a neighbour and you rewarded me for it. There was a—I don't know how you'd

put it in words—a very pleasant atmosphere. I wanted
things to go well.

PAUL. Naturally, sir.

ABBOTT. But I've no complaints at all. It went off with
a—a sprightliness. Yes. Sunny's the word.

MRS. MUNNING. Thank you very much, Mr. Abbott.

ABBOTT. But mind you, Mrs. Munning, you don't always
do it.

PAUL. I'm sure we try to make no difference.

ABBOTT. You don't always succeed as you did for me.
There was a jolly feeling that I'm sure has not been there for
some time past. Still, I was pleased, and I've told others I
was pleased.

PAUL. Thanks very much. We *have* had more orders in
this last fortnight.

ABBOTT. Well, I daresay some of them are due to me.
Don't let me down now I've been recommending you. I can
get out this way ?

ZACK (*opening door*). Yes, Mr. Abbott.

ABBOTT (*ignoring him, to* PAUL). Good-day, Munning.

PAUL and MRS. MUNNING. Good-day, sir.

(*Exit* ABBOTT.)

MRS. MUNNING. Well, here's a change.

PAUL. He's not the first who's talked like that these
last few times. But why they do it is a mystery to me.

MRS. MUNNING. I've got a guess. Jenny, you've brought
us luck.

VIRGINIA. I ?

MRS. MUNNING. It's since you came that things have
taken this turn.

VIRGINIA. I'm very glad to hear it, aunt.

Mrs. Munning. You've been a blessing to us.

Paul. I think I'll send some more accounts out, mother. They might fetch other people's money in like Mr. Abbott's.

Virginia. Oh yes. I'm in your way here.

Mrs. Munning. And you're not. You're never in the way.

Paul. As if I'd mean a thing like that to you, Virginia.

Virginia. But I was just going, aunt. I've something upstairs that I want to bring for Zack.

Mrs. Munning. Zack?

Virginia. You'd forgotten it's his birthday.

(PAUL *sits at the table.*)

Mrs. Munning. No, I hadn't, Jenny. Mothers don't forget a thing like that. But I'd not seen cause to mention it.

Virginia. I'll get Zack's present. (*She opens door.*) By the way, wasn't it at Mr. Abbott's wedding that Zack began to go again?

Mrs. Munning. I fancy it was.

Virginia. And he's been going to the others since?

Mrs. Munning. Yes. But he's still on trial. Why, Jenny?

Virginia. I only wondered.

(*Exit* VIRGINIA.)

Paul. Get on with your work, Zack.

Zack. Yes, Paul. (*He turns the handle once or twice, and is then occupied testing the result.*)

Mrs. Munning. Come here a minute, Paul. You're not that busy.

PAUL. I'm not busy at all. I just made a show of it before Virginia. A good thing she heard him talk like that

MRS. MUNNING. I'll tell you something better for the business than Mr. Abbott's talk.

PAUL. If you'll tell me what it is that makes people say one thing of us one week and change their minds the next, you'll be doing me a good turn.

MRS. MUNNING. I'll do you a better turn. I'd a chat with Virginia in her room last night.

PAUL. I heard your voices going late. You kept me awake.

MRS. MUNNING. Well, it was worth it, Paul. I knew they were well off, but there's more than I thought. The girl's got money of her own besides her mother's.

(ZACK *turns the handle.*)

PAUL. Some folk get all the luck.

MRS. MUNNING. Well ?

PAUL. Well what ?

MRS. MUNNING. Don't you take me, Paul ?

(ZACK *works the machine.* MRS. MUNNING *turns on him.*)

Oh, will you hush your noise, Zack ? Get away out of this while I talk to Paul.

ZACK (*going* L.). Yes, mother.

PAUL. Go round to Bealey's and ask him if those nails have come. Don't be all day.

ZACK. No, Paul. (*He turns to door and goes out.*)

MRS. MUNNING. Look here, Paul, you could do a lot to this business if you had the capital. We could start a temperance hotel and give up the joinery altogether. Zack could clean boots.

PAUL. Aye. If——

MRS. MUNNING. She's got it.

PAUL. Well for her.

MRS. MUNNING. You're not slow to see your interests as a rule.

PAUL. Slow ? I'd call it quick myself and very quick. I've known the girl a fortnight.

MRS. MUNNING. Oh, you do see what I'm driving at.

PAUL. I saw it days ago.

MRS. MUNNING. And anything the matter with it ?

PAUL. Only Virginia.

MRS. MUNNING. What's wrong with her ?

PAUL. She don't show willing.

MRS. MUNNING. Have you asked ?

PAUL. Asked ? I haven't. It's not a thing to rush at, mother. I've to look at every side before I take a leap like that.

MRS. MUNNING. What are you frightened of ?

PAUL. I wouldn't like to get refused. I don't so much as know she thinks of me at all.

MRS. MUNNING. And what do you think I'm doing all these days ? I've done nothing else but keep you in her mind. She knows it all from A to Z. Why, only yesterday I gave her the Bible to look at, and you know what's written in the front of it. There's every prize you ever won at school on record with the date and——

PAUL. And what she found in the Bible was that it's Zack's birthday to-day and she's giving him a present.

MRS. MUNNING. Well, she's got a kind heart. I saw her give a beggar sixpence yesterday.

PAUL. That isn't kindness. It's extravagance, and I've no taste for a wife who throws her money away.

MRS. MUNNING. She couldn't throw it if she hadn't got it first. And I'd trust you to let her know that charity begins at home when she's your wife.

PAUL. There's something in that.

MRS. MUNNING. There's all in it. I say we've got a golden chance, and I don't know what you're shirking for. Our luck's well in all round with people talking sensibly about us and the orders coming in.

PAUL. That's not to say Virginia 'ull have me.

MRS. MUNNING. You'll get to know by asking, Paul. And I tell you she's ripe for it.

PAUL. Ripe ?

MRS. MUNNING. The girl's in love. She's got the signs of it all over her. It only needs a bit of enterprise from you, and all's as good as done.

PAUL. I've seen no signs of love. She's got a thumping appetite, if that's your meaning.

MRS. MUNNING. Where's your eyes ? The girl's another creature since she's been with us.

PAUL. The country air did that. I thought love made them pale.

MRS. MUNNING. Quit talking, Paul. Are you in love with any other girl ?

PAUL. What, me in love ? I've got more sense.

MRS. MUNNING. Then marry Virginia.

PAUL. All right. I'll try.

(*Enter* VIRGINIA. *She has a small brown-papered parcel.*)

VIRGINIA. Oh ! is Zack not here ?

MRS. MUNNING. He's gone out on an errand. Did you want him ?

VIRGINIA. Yes. To give him this. But it will do later. (*She turns away.*)

MRS. MUNNING. Oh, don't go, Jenny.

VIRGINIA. But Paul's busy here.

MRS. MUNNING. Paul's never too busy to have some time for you. But I've got to see Sally myself, so I'll leave you two together.

(*Exit* MRS. MUNNING.)

PAUL. I'll make you comfortable here. (*He fusses at the chairs and places one for her.*)

VIRGINIA. Oh, please don't trouble, Paul.

PAUL. There's no trouble about it, Jenny. It's always a pleasure to do things for you.

VIRGINIA. Why, Paul, I didn't know.

PAUL. Know what ?

VIRGINIA. That you did things for me.

PAUL. You didn't ? Well, I haven't boasted up to now.

VIRGINIA. No. Then it's you, and I've been thinking it was Zack.

PAUL. Thought what was Zack ?

VIRGINIA. I thought Zack brought the roses that I'm always finding in my room and——

PAUL (*uneasy, but bluffing*). Zack ? Did you ever see him doing it ?

VIRGINIA. No. And it was you. (*Hand out.*) Paul, I apologize.

PAUL. Apologize ? For what ? (*He touches her hand.*)

VIRGINIA. I imagined you too businesslike to think of doing anything like that.

PAUL. Well, Jenny, you were wrong that time. I've

got an eye to business, but I'm not quite blind to other things. I've eyes to see the roses coming to your cheeks to match the roses in your room.

VIRGINIA. Yes. I do look better for my stay with you, don't I ?

PAUL. It's working wonders, Jenny. The country is the place for you.

VIRGINIA. I shall be sorry to go.

PAUL. Oh, that's too bad. To talk of going.

VIRGINIA. Not yet, of course.

PAUL. And not at all, if I'd my way.

VIRGINIA. Not at all ?

PAUL. Are you so set on towns ?

VIRGINIA. I live in one.

PAUL. Yes, but I wonder why. It beats me why you and your mother want to live in ugliness with noise and bad air, Jenny. Where's the need for it ?

VIRGINIA. Friends. Associations. That's all.

PAUL. You'd never want for friends anywhere.

VIRGINIA. But I've to think of mother. She's like an old tree, firmly rooted and she's hard to move. So we stay where we are.

PAUL. And you'll grow ill again.

VIRGINIA. Oh no. I shall be all right now.

PAUL. You'd be better here.

VIRGINIA. I can't stay here for ever.

PAUL. We might find out a way, Jenny.

VIRGINIA. How ?

PAUL. Don't you see ? (*Takes her hand.*)

VIRGINIA. Paul ! I never thought of this.

PAUL. I've thought of nothing else since I set eyes on you.

VIRGINIA (*withdrawing hand*). But I must think a little now and—and confess.

PAUL. Confess! You mean that in the town——

VIRGINIA. Not in the town, Paul. Here!

PAUL. You don't mean——

VIRGINIA. Yes. I thought I was so clever and could see what you and aunt were blind to. It was just a bad mistake, but I have had Zack in my mind a lot. So much, Paul, that I didn't think of you, or if I did it was as something not quite—— I liked Zack, and I fancied you were wrong to make so little of him. Why, even now, when Mr. Abbott came to say how pleased he'd been and you were puzzled at it all, I thought I'd guessed the cause and put it down to Zack.

PAUL. Well—that's a queer idea.

VIRGINIA. I know it must seem queer to you. I'm sorry I was stupid, Paul. Of course you must know best, living with Zack for all these years. But—isn't it just a little hard to keep him without money?

PAUL. You don't know all the truth. We do. We've had experience of Zack.

VIRGINIA. Yes. I suppose I'm being rash again.

PAUL. I think we've got the size of him, Virginia. He's bone-lazy.

VIRGINIA. Yes.

PAUL. Well, that's Zack. But I was talking of myself —and you.

VIRGINIA. You'll have to give me time for that, please, Paul. I made a false start and I have to see things all over again before I get them right.

PAUL. You're not convinced that Zack's a fool.

VIRGINIA. I have your word now, Paul. But that doesn't quite mean that I—I —

PAUL. That you love me.

VIRGINIA. It doesn't follow, does it, Paul ?

PAUL. I hoped it might.

VIRGINIA. Some day, when I'm used to knowing that it's you who've done the little things that made me happy here, it might come, Paul. I cannot say just yet.

(*The door* C. *is burst open violently and* JOE WRIGLEY *stands in the doorway. Behind him, both very reluctant, are* ZACK *and* MARTHA. JOE *is a big man, with his left arm in a sling. He is strong in body and purpose, and has a useful gift of sly humour. He can dominate, and in the ensuing scene, he does. He advances.* ZACK *closes the door, and he and* MARTHA *try to look effaced in the background.*)

WRIGLEY. Good morning.

PAUL. Wrigley !

WRIGLEY. That's me.

PAUL. Get out of this. There's nothing here for you.

WRIGLEY. I beg to differ, Mr. Paul. We've things to settle here, have you and me.

PAUL. Well, you can't settle them now. I'm busy.

WRIGLEY. I'm not, and so I'll wait your pleasure.

PAUL. I've finished with you, Wrigley.

WRIGLEY. No, you haven't, Mr. Paul. You only think you have.

VIRGINIA. I'd better go, Paul.

PAUL. No. I'll get rid of him.

WRIGLEY. When things are settled, you'll get rid of me. And not before.

PAUL. You're trespassing in here. I tell you to get out.

WRIGLEY. You'll do yourself no good by quarrelling.

It's him I've come about. Him and her. Your Zack and my Martha.

PAUL. Zack? What about him?

WRIGLEY. They've got to be married.

PAUL. What!

VIRGINIA. Oh, how horrid! (*She turns away.*)

ZACK (*following her*). No, no! Please, Virginia! It isn't true.

WRIGLEY (*growling*). What isn't true?

ZACK. I mean you're twisting it.

WRIGLEY. You're going to marry her.

ZACK. Yes. If you say so, but you make it sound so bad the way you're putting it. I mean, you'll make Virginia think that I——

WRIGLEY. And who cares what she thinks?

ZACK. I care, Mr. Wrigley, I do indeed.

WRIGLEY. Oh! Then you're blacker than I took you for. Carrying on with two young women at once.

VIRGINIA. Upon my word!

WRIGLEY. It's he that said he cared, miss. It wasn't me.

PAUL. Let's have this from the beginning, Wrigley.

WRIGLEY. Beginning? I reckon this began when the Lord made him a male and her a female.

PAUL. Oh yes. That's very funny, but——

WRIGLEY. It's not. There's nothing funny in the ways of sex. They've been the worry of the world for ever since the world grew bigger than the Garden of Eden, and if you think they're funny, you've a lot to learn.

PAUL. Wrigley, do you know who you're speaking to?

WRIGLEY. Aye. Brother of my future son-in-law. Makes you a kind of sideways son of mine yourself.

PAUL. We'll have this tale from Zack if you won't tell it straight.

WRIGLEY. I'd rather; and I'll just be here to know he tells it straight.

(WRIGLEY *sits*.)

PAUL. Now, Zack. No. Wait a minute. Mother had best be in at this. (*Opening door.*) Mother!

VIRGINIA. And I had better not. (*She follows to door.*)

PAUL. Are you afraid to know the worst of him ? (*Calling.*) Mother!

MRS. MUNNING (*off*). I'm coming, Paul.

VIRGINIA. Oh, Zack, Zack, I am so disappointed in you.

ZACK. I meant no harm, Virginia. It's a thing that's grown from nothing like, and I don't know how it grew so fast.

MRS. MUNNING (*entering*). What is it, Paul ?

PAUL. Zack and Joe Wrigley's girl. Now go on, Zack. What have you done ?

ZACK. I've got to speak it out before you all and with Virginia hearing, too ?

VIRGINIA. I'll go.

PAUL. Why should you ?

VIRGINIA. Because I prefer it, Paul.

(*Exit* VIRGINIA.)

MRS. MUNNING. We're waiting, Zack.

ZACK. Well, there isn't much to tell that you don't know about, mother.

MRS. MUNNING. I !

ZACK. You started the whole thing off.

MRS. MUNNING. When ?

ZACK. You mind that day when Martha came to tell us Joe had broke his arm and Martha took on so in our parlour.

MRS. MUNNING. Well?

ZACK. Well, that's it.

MRS. MUNNING. That!

ZACK. Yes. You came in when I was trying to console her and——

MRS. MUNNING. I caught you kissing her, if that's what you mean.

WRIGLEY. Ah! That's a point. I'd been waiting for that to come.

ZACK. I know I kissed her, but it wasn't a meaning kiss. She was blubbing and she wouldn't hush and so I kissed her like I'd kiss a baby to console it.

WRIGLEY. You kissed her. That's enough.

ZACK. But it weren't for pleasure, Mr. Wrigley. She was too wet.

MRS. MUNNING. He kissed her all right. I saw it. What about it?

WRIGLEY. He's got to marry her. That's all.

MRS. MUNNING. Now what has kissing a girl to do with marriage?

WRIGLEY. A lot. He's going to marry her because you said so.

MRS. MUNNING. I?

ZACK. That's the trouble, mother. You did say something, joking like. You said, " When's the wedding? " and I joked back and said, " About a month," and Martha took it serious and told her father, and he told other people and it's all over the village. It's expected of me now, and I suppose——

MRS. MUNNING. Be quiet, Zack.

ZACK. You told me to tell you.

MRS. MUNNING. Keep your mouth shut when I tell you. You only open it to give yourself away.

WRIGLEY. You needn't trouble, missus. He's done all that.

MRS. MUNNING. Done what? You know he'd no intentions, and he hasn't any now. He's made no promises.

WRIGLEY. He's promised and he's made her presents.

MRS. MUNNING. You'll have to prove that first.

WRIGLEY. Prove? Where's that parcel, Martha?

(MARTHA *comes timidly forward with it.*)

Open it. See that?

MRS. MUNNING. This? Crusts of bread and bits of meat!

WRIGLEY. That's it. Bread you baked and meat from what you had for dinner yesterday.

MRS. MUNNING. How did you come by this?

ZACK. I saved them from my food. She told me she was always hungry and I felt that sorry for her.

MRS. MUNNING (*giving the parcel to* MARTHA). You're too soft to live. Well, that's only giving charity, Joe Wrigley.

WRIGLEY. With lots of folk it might be, but it's something else than charity when one of your family starts giving things away.

MRS. MUNNING. It's nowt to do with marrying and promising, so what it is.

WRIGLEY. He promised her not half an hour ago in Tim Bealey's shop, with witnesses and all. There was Tim Bealey there and his missus and the errand lad and me.

MRS. MUNNING. Is that true, Zack?

ZACK. I did say something, mother.

MRS. MUNNING. You silly fool !

ZACK. But it was only to save argument. I do hate argument when people have a voice as loud as Joe's.

MRS. MUNNING. That means you forced him, Wrigley.

WRIGLEY. It means he promised before witnesses, and I'll take good care he keeps his word.

MRS. MUNNING. Come here, Martha. Do you want to marry him ?

WRIGLEY. Of course she does.

MRS. MUNNING. Let the girl speak for herself.

MARTHA. I'd like to, Mrs. Munning. Only not if Zack don't want as well. I'd not expect it.

WRIGLEY. But I expect it.

PAUL. Yes, Joe, we know it's you we've got to thank for this.

WRIGLEY. I reckon it's me all right. You'll think twice before you sack a man for getting hurt another time. I'll teach you something.

PAUL (quietly). Will you ? By marrying your girl to Zack ?

WRIGLEY. That's it. I'll break your pride.

PAUL. It might break you. I wouldn't swear that this wouldn't make me, Joe.

MARTHA (up to ZACK). I didn't go to do it, Zack. I don't want to be no trouble to nobody.

MRS. MUNNING. Do you want her, Zack ?

ZACK. I'd rather not say, mother. I wouldn't like to hurt her feelings.

PAUL. Do you want to marry her ?

ZACK. I'd rather drown myself.

MARTHA. Oh !

ZACK (*to her*). There, there, Martha. I didn't mean to hurt you. There!

MRS. MUNNING. Keep your great hands to yourself, Zack, can't you?

ZACK. I've hurt her feelings, mother.

MRS. MUNNING. And I'll hurt yours if you don't do what I tell you sharp.

WRIGLEY. Come, Mrs. Munning. What's to do with a chap putting his arm round the girl he's going to marry?

MRS. MUNNING. He's just about the same chance of marrying her as you have of coming back to work here, Joe.

WRIGLEY. I fancy both our chances then.

MRS. MUNNING. You'd lose your money.

WRIGLEY. I think not, Mrs. Munning. I've a notion that you'll weigh things up and come to seeing this my way. I've not come here to quarrel with my relations to be, but I'll just point out that Wilson's of Norton are getting business off you every day and you can't afford a scandal in your line of trade.

MRS. MUNNING. Be careful, Wrigley. Threats of that kind have a nasty name.

WRIGLEY. I'm not afraid of names. Come here, Martha. We've given them enough to think about.

MARTHA. Yes, father.

WRIGLEY. I'll look in later for your answer. (*Opens door.*)

PAUL. You needn't. You can have it now.

MRS. MUNNING. You can. I'll give it you. It's this, that——

PAUL. Zack can go with you now to see the vicar, Joe.

WRIGLEY. Eh?

MRS. MUNNING. What?

ZACK. Paul!

MRS. MUNNING. Paul, are you mad ?

ZACK. But I don't want to marry her. I don't indeed.

PAUL. You've made your bed and you'll lie on it. I'll stir no hand to save you.

MRS. MUNNING. But, Paul——

PAUL. I've got my reasons, mother, and they're sound.

ZACK. There's no great hurry, is there, Paul ?

PAUL. If a thing's to be done, it's best done quick. We'll have the banns put up on Sunday.

WRIGLEY. You're in a mighty haste. It's giving things a queerish twist to me.

PAUL. When I've to take a dose of physic, I don't play round because it's got a filthy taste. I get it down.

ZACK. But it's my physic, Paul.

PAUL. You'll do as you're told.

MARTHA. I'm sure I'll try to make you a good wife, Zack.

ZACK. If it comes to the worst, I'll try and all. But we might both try and make a mess of it for all we tried. I'm against this, Martha, and it's no good wrapping up the truth. I don't favour it and I can't see sense in it at all.

PAUL. You've gone a bit too far to talk like that, my lad.

ZACK. I wouldn't say I'd gone at all, not knowingly, I mean. It's happened like, somehow, and I'll say this much or brast for it. It'll be the mistake of your life, Martha. I'm not cut out for a husband of yours. If ever you get wed——

PAUL. She's wedding you.

ZACK. Well, I don't favour it. I've as good a right to my opinion as anybody else and I say it's not fair doing to Martha.

WRIGLEY. Is Martha all you're thinking of ?

ZACK. There's me as well, and I tell you what I told you down in Bealey's shop. I'm always one to take the short road out of trouble and I'm ready to oblige you. But I don't like it and the more I think about Martha the worse it looks to saddle her with me. Martha's the helpless sort and I'm the helpless sort and you don't make two soft people into strong by wedding them together. She'd try to lean on me and I'd try to lean on her and there'd be nothing there to lean on. It's like trying to make weak tea strong by watering the pot. Martha'll only wed with trouble when she weds a gormless chap like me, and I don't favour it. I see no sense in it at all, and it's no use saying I do, because I don't.

MRS. MUNNING. And I don't see the sense in doing things to please Joe Wrigley.

PAUL. I'm doing this to please myself, not him. What are you waiting for, Wrigley ? You've got your answer.

WRIGLEY. I dunno.

PAUL. Then don't wait. If you want to see Mr. Andrews, it's a good time to catch him now before his lunch.

WRIGLEY. Come along.

(WRIGLEY *and* MARTHA *move towards door.*)

ZACK. Paul ! You're going to have me called in church ?

PAUL. It's the usual place.

ZACK. Me and Martha Wrigley ! And everybody listening !

PAUL. Take him with you, Joe.

ZACK (*going slowly*). Well, I don't favour it at all. I'll do my best for Martha, but I'm a silly best for any girl. I've got no heart in this.

(MRS. MUNNING *goes up towards* ZACK. PAUL *stops her with a gesture. Exit* ZACK, *after* WRIGLEY *and* MARTHA.)

Mrs. Munning (*turning angrily.*) You're crossing me in this. I've not said much so far because there's time to stop it yet.

Paul. You won't want to stop it, mother.

Mrs. Munning. Won't I ? I'm not particular fond of Zack, but he's my son as much as you, and I've no taste to see a Munning standing up in church with a daughter of Joe Wrigley's.

Paul. I've just two things to say to that. The first is that you started it with joking about marriage, and the second's what you're planning now for Virginia and me.

Mrs. Munning. Virginia ?

Paul. I've had that talk with her

Mrs. Munning. Well ? Is it right ?

Paul. It isn't right, and it was very wrong. I've got her coming round. No more than that. But this affair of Zack's chimes in with what we want.

Mrs. Munning. What's Zack to do with her ?

Paul. That's where the queerness comes. What do you think, mother ?

Mrs. Munning. I'm getting past all thought to-day.

Paul. She'd him in mind.

Mrs. Munning. Zack ! Well, I don't know ! What's Zack been doing that takes her fancy ?

Paul. Did you ever know Zack do anything ? Oh, she told me one thing. He's been putting flowers in her room.

Mrs. Munning. In her room ! The impudence.

Paul. I put those flowers there. You understand ?

Mrs. Munning. *You ?* Oh, I see.

Paul. And I'll tell you something else. She thinks the weddings have got a better name because Zack's going to them now,

MRS. MUNNING. But Zack does nothing but break things when he goes.

PAUL. I'm telling you what she thinks, not what we know. She's got a fancy picture of him in her mind, and while it's there, she'll never marry me. That's why he'll marry Martha.

MRS. MUNNING. I'm not at ease about it, Paul.

PAUL. Whose scheme was it for me to marry Jenny? Mine or yours?

MRS. MUNNING. It's mine, I know.

PAUL. Then you shouldn't scheme if you're not prepared to put things through. I am prepared. I didn't think seriously of this until you set me on. But now I'm on, I'm on, and it'll not be Zack will stop me, neither.

MRS. MUNNING. We'll have to set them up.

PAUL. That won't cost much.

MRS. MUNNING. I'll never bear the sight of Zack living along of Martha in the village here.

PAUL. We might get over that. It's costing something, but there'll be Virginia's money soon, and so——

MRS. MUNNING. What's in your mind?

PAUL. A clean sweep, mother. Getting rid of them. It's much the best. Zack's never any use to us.

MRS. MUNNING. Get rid?

PAUL. We'll emigrate them when they're married.

MRS. MUNNING. You're thinking fast.

PAUL. Leave it to me, mother. I'll arrange it. Yes. It's all plain sailing now. Zack married and in Canada, and me and Jenny here with you. I'll see that steamship agency at Bollington to-morrow and find out the cost.

(ZACK *enters.*)

What on earth——? You've never seen Mr. Andrews in this time?

ZACK. No.

PAUL. Then what do you mean by coming back?

ZACK. Well, I wasn't satisfied we were doing right, Paul, and I got a notion as I went along with Joe and Martha.

PAUL. A notion?

ZACK. I made my mind up I'd consult somebody before it got to doing things so final as the banns.

PAUL. But we've decided.

ZACK. I know you have, but I'm still doubtful, and I thought I'd ask Virginia to tell me what to do.

MRS. MUNNING. Ask Virginia?

ZACK. Yes. Tell her all about it and just see what she advises me to do. I've a great respect for her opinions.

PAUL. More than you have for ours?

ZACK. I can't say that until I know what her opinion is.

MRS. MUNNING. She'll be disgusted with you.

PAUL. You'll keep your foolishness to yourself, Zack, do you hear?

ZACK. I'm hard put to it to see I have been foolish, Paul. Virginia will tell me, I expect.

MRS. MUNNING. Where have you left Joe Wrigley? At the Vicarage?

ZACK. No. At the "Bunch of Grapes."

PAUL. The "Bunch of Grapes"! The crazy fool. Drinking when he'd a job like this to do.

ZACK. I suppose he'd have a drink.

PAUL. Oh, yes, he'd money for that. They've never any money, but there's always some for drink.

ZACK. It wasn't his fault, Paul. I gave it him,

MRS. MUNNING. You! Where did you get money from?

ZACK. I gave him sixpence that Paul gave me this morning for a birthday present.

MRS. MUNNING. Paul gave you sixpence!

PAUL. Yes, I did, as it happens. For a purpose, though. (*Turns on* ZACK.) What gets me is Joe Wrigley's letting loose of you at any price.

ZACK. I gave him an explanation of that. I told him I'd forgotten something important.

PAUL. And he believed you for sixpence?

ZACK. But I *had* forgotten something, Paul.

PAUL. What?

ZACK. Well——

MRS. MUNNING. What's that you're hiding behind you all this time?

ZACK. I'd forgotten these. (*He discloses a small bunch of roses.*) They're wild roses from the hedge and I came back to put them in Virginia's room when she's not there, same as I have done every day, only I'd forgotten them this morning.

MRS. MUNNING. You can just leave off doing it then. Virginia's room! Have you no sense of decency?

ZACK. I'm sure she likes them, mother.

PAUL (*anxiously*). She never told you so?

ZACK. No, but I've seen her smiling at me and——

MRS. MUNNING. She may well smile. Your ways would make a cat laugh.

ZACK. I'll—I'll throw the flowers away. (*He turns towards door.*)

PAUL. Give me those flowers! (*Following him to door.*)

ZACK. But——

PAUL. Go back and get your business done,

(Enter Virginia *from the house. She has a small parcel. There is a conflict of wills at the street door. Then* Zack *steps into the room again.* Paul *closes the door.* Virginia *notices the flowers. She goes towards* Paul, *smiling.)*

Paul. Oh! You've—you've caught me this time.

Virginia. But you needn't look ashamed, Paul.

Paul. I didn't know I did. I'll—I'll take them away now.

Virginia. That's very sweet of you.

*(*Zack *watches agape.* Paul *goes out with the roses.)*

Virginia. Now, Zack, I don't think you deserve it, but I brought your birthday present down, and here it is. A shaving-set.

Zack. I'm sorry, but I haven't got a coin to give you now for luck.

Virginia. That doesn't matter now.

Zack. Oh, Jenny!

Mrs. Munning. I'd think not, too, with you disgraced. Haven't you got a word of thanks for your razor ?

Zack. Yes. It's the best gift you could make me, Jenny.

Virginia. And you promise me you'll use it, Zack ?

Zack. I'll use it right enough. I'll cut my throat with it.

Mrs. Munning. Zack! He doesn't know what he's saying, Jenny.

Zack. I do know, and I mean it, too. *(Tearing at paper of the parcel.)*

Virginia *(dryly).* You'd have some trouble, Zack. It's a safety razor.

ZACK. You're all against me, all of you, and I don't care what happens to me.

VIRGINIA. Zack, listen to me. I'm not against you, though I'm very, very sorry for what you've done.

ZACK. I haven't done anything and nobody will let me tell you and——

MRS. MUNNING. Your cousin doesn't want to hear about that, Zack.

ZACK. You're trying to stop her hearing and I'm going to tell her now. She's got it all so wrong. I know I'm not an angel in trousers, but I'm not a wrong 'un neither, and——

MRS. MUNNING. That will do, Zack. You've said enough.

ZACK. You'll none of you be sorry when I'm dead.

VIRGINIA. I should be very sorry, Zack. What is it that you want to tell me ?

ZACK. Mother won't let me speak.

VIRGINIA. I'm sure she will. She's leaving us together now, so that you may tell me what you want to say.

MRS. MUNNING. I doubt it's safe for you, Jenny. He's a bit beside himself.

VIRGINIA. It's quite the best way, aunt. To let him open his heart to me. He'll be much better after that.

MRS. MUNNING. He'll tell a pack of lies to get the soft side of you.

VIRGINIA. I'll make all due allowances, aunt, if you will leave me with him now.

MRS. MUNNING. I'm loth to, Jenny.

VIRGINIA. Then Zack and I will take a walk and he shall tell me as we go.

MRS. MUNNING. Oh, if you're keen set like that, I'll go.

VIRGINIA. Thank you, aunt.

MRS. MUNNING (*at door*). But don't you go believing half of what he says.

(*Exit* MRS. MUNNING.)

ZACK. I'm wonderful obliged to you, Jenny. I'll get some good advice now.

VIRGINIA. Sit down and tell me what you want to.

ZACK. I dunno where to begin. It's so mixed up. But I'm not a desperate bad lad, Virginia. I'm really not.

VIRGINIA. No. Begin at the beginning, Zack.

ZACK. It's like this, Jenny. On the day you came, Martha Wrigley came here to let us know her father had broke his arm, and I——

(*The street door opens violently and* WRIGLEY *enters. Silently he goes to* ZACK *and points to door.*)

ZACK. I'm busy just now, Joe.

WRIGLEY. Are you coming ?

ZACK. But—— Yes, Joe.

VIRGINIA (*stopping* ZACK *as he goes*). I want Zack, Mr. Wrigley.

WRIGLEY. You can have him when I've done with him.

VIRGINIA. Mr. Wrigley, I ask you as a favour.

WRIGLEY. I'm sorry to disoblige a lady, but my affair comes first.

VIRGINIA. I think not.

ZACK. Let me go with him, Jenny.

VIRGINIA. But, Zack, you were going to tell me——

ZACK. I know. But he'll only argue, and I do hate argument. It wouldn't be any good, Virginia. My luck's dead out.

WRIGLEY (*by door*). Come on.
ZACK. Yes, Joe. Oh, what a birthday !

(WRIGLEY *and* ZACK *go out.*)

CURTAIN.

ACT III

The parlour as ACT I. *The time is seven o'clock on a sunny evening three weeks later. The stage is empty. Then* MARTHA *opens a door, looks in, enters, comes* C., *hesitates and sits. She is dressed in her best and looks like a country servant girl on a Sunday evening. She carries a small handbag.* SALLY *enters from house.*

SALLY (*crossing and pulling up short on seeing* MARTHA). Well, I never did see the like of you, Martha Wrigley. Strolling in and sitting you down as if you owned the place.

MARTHA. Are you speaking to me ?

SALLY. I'm not addressing my remarks to the table.

MARTHA (*with great hauteur*). I believe I'm speaking to Mrs. Munning's kitchen-maid.

SALLY. Kitchen-maid ! I'm a lady-help. And you couldn't get a job at cleaning steps yourself.

MARTHA. I want some of your impudence, my girl.

SALLY. Impudence ! From me to you ! I've known when you came begging a slice of bread from my lunch when we were at school, and——

MARTHA. Times change, don't they, Sally ? I'm sitting in the parlour now, and your place is in the kitchen. You'll keep it, too.

SALLY. You know very well I'm only obliging Mrs. Munning temporarily.

MARTHA. I know you're idling your time in here and if you don't want me to show you up to Mrs. Munning for a dawdling slouch, you'll keep the sweet side of me.

SALLY. You do think you're some one because you're going to marry Zack. It might be Mr. Paul the fuss you make.

MARTHA (*rising*). It's a pity that folk can't control themselves.

SALLY. If that's meant for me, let me tell you I never lost control of myself in my life.

MARTHA. If the cap fits you can put it on.

SALLY. You'll please to tell me what you mean by that, Martha Wrigley.

MARTHA. Everybody knows you'd hopes of Zack yourself. You're only showing your jealousy.

SALLY. Me jealous of you! You'll take that back. Do you hear? You'll take that back.

MARTHA. Not me. It's a well-known fact.

SALLY. Who says?

MARTHA. I say.

SALLY. Then I call you a liar. You're a liar, and a mean, spiteful spitting cat, and——

(MARTHA *gives back before her.* ZACK *enters.*)

MARTHA. Zack!

ZACK. Hullo, Martha! I just came in here for a bit of a sit-down. I favour a spell of peace and quiet at the close of the day.

(*He just touches* MARTHA *without affection in passing and sits.*)

SALLY. And all day too.

MARTHA. You hold your hush, Sally Teale. Am I to come in here to be insulted by your servant, Zack ?

ZACK. Nay, I've got no servant that I ever heard of.

MARTHA. Sally.

ZACK. Eh, Martha, Sally's a decent body. She'd never insult nobody.

MARTHA. Are you going to take her side against me ?

ZACK. I've not seen anything to take anybody's side about as yet.

SALLY. She says I'm jealous and she'll take it back.

MARTHA. I won't. As true as true, you are.

SALLY. I'm not.

MARTHA. You are.

SALLY. I'm not. I'm not. I'm not.

(ZACK *rises, comes between, puts finger in mouth and whistles.*)

SALLY. I'm not.

ZACK. That's enough, lass. Whistle's gone. I'm referee and I look at it like this. You can't both be right.

SALLY. No, I'm——

ZACK. And you can't both be wrong.

MARTHA. She's——

ZACK. So it's a draw.

MARTHA. That doesn't help. She called me a liar.

ZACK (*impressed*). No. Did you, Sally ?

SALLY. Yes, I did. and——

ZACK. I'm sorry to hear that of you, Sally.

SALLY (*contrite*). Well, she shouldn't have said——

ZACK. Maybe she spoke beyond her meaning. You did, didn't you, Martha ?

MARTHA. I spoke hasty.

ZACK (*to* SALLY). And you answered hasty, didn't you ?
SALLY. I might.
ZACK. I thought so. Haste ! It's the cause of half the
trouble in the world. I never hurry. It's a principle
with me.
MARTHA (*tearfully*). Zack, I'm sorry I put on airs. I
won't do it again. (*Comes to him. He puts arm round her*).
SALLY. I'll—I'll not lose my temper again, Zack. (*Comes
to him. He puts his other arm round her.*)
ZACK. There, there, Martha. There, there, Sally. I
never did believe in arguing. It's wear and tear for nothing,
and——

(VIRGINIA *and* MRS. MUNNING *enter,* VIRGINIA *in light dress,
with hat and gloves.*)

VIRGINIA. Oh !
MRS. MUNNING. Going in for being a Mormon, Zack ?
ZACK. No, mother. I dunno how it is, cousin Virginia,
but the awkwardest things do keep happening to me. I was
only reconciling them like.
MRS. MUNNING. You haven't done the bedrooms for
the night, Sally.
SALLY. I'm on my way there now.
MRS. MUNNING. You'll arrive a lot sooner if you'll try
going upstairs.
(SALLY *is about to reply, thinks better of it and goes out.*)
ZACK. I'm the unluckiest chap alive, Virginia. I'd
give the world to have you thinking well of me, and things
fall out wrong road every time.
MRS. MUNNING. That'll do, Zack. Martha's waiting
to speak to me. What is it, Martha ?
MARTHA (*opening her bag*). This is what I came in for,

Mrs. Munning. Your invitation to the wedding. Oh !
(*She drops some cards.*)

Mrs. Munning. Pick them up, Zack.

(Zack *picks them up.*)

Martha. I thought Zack and me might go round to-
night delivering them.

(Zack, *on his knee picking up cards, reverently kisses the hem
of* Virginia's *skirt.*)

Mrs. Munning. Oh yes. (*Sharply.*) What are you
doing, Zack ?

Zack (*scrambling up*). Picking up cards. (*Giving them
to* Mrs. Munning.)

Mrs Munning. Why, you've had cards printed. (*Returns cards to* Martha.)

Martha. They are stylish, aren't they ? (*Giving a
card*). That's yours, Mrs. Munning. And I brought you
one, Miss Virginia.

Virginia. Thanks.

Mrs. Munning. Waste of money.

Martha. You can't be genteel without spending a bit
of money. A wedding's a wedding, Mrs. Munning, and folk
have to spread themselves sometimes. Are you ready,
Zack ?

Zack. I'm not so anxious, Martha. It'll mean a lot of
walking.

Mrs. Munning. I suppose you'd rather good money
went on postage ?

Zack. All right, mother. I'll go. Only you know,
Martha, you're tying this knot firm. A printed card's an
awful binding thing.

MARTHA. My father's got to see there's no mistake.

ZACK. He's doing pretty well so far.

MARTHA. Yes. My wedding-dress is coming home to-night, too. I'll show it you if you like.

ZACK (*swallowing, then*). I'm like a cat on hot bricks till I see that dress.

(MARTHA *and* ZACK *go out.*)

VIRGINIA. Poor Zack !

MRS. MUNNING. Fools pay for their folly. Did you come down for your walk with Paul ?

VIRGINIA. Yes. It's about the usual time.

MRS. MUNNING. He'll be late this evening. He'd to go to Bollington this afternoon, but he'll bring you back a fairing, Jenny. He mostly went on your account.

VIRGINIA. On mine ?

MRS. MUNNING. Paul's fretting because the roses he's putting in your room each day aren't good enough for you. He's gone to Bollington to see if he can't find better at the flower shop there.

VIRGINIA (*coldly*). He needn't have troubled, aunt.

MRS. MUNNING. Paul doesn't count it trouble to do things for you.

VIRGINIA. So he's told me.

MRS. MUNNING. Well, truth's truth, and I'm not bound to hide it. He's missed his proper bedtime every night with seeking roses here to suit him. They've got to be so fine and large before they'll do for Paul.

(SALLY *enters with a vase of very faded roses in her hand.*)

SALLY. Do you want these leaving in your room any longer, Miss Virginia ? They're that faded and done they'll stink the place out soon.

VIRGINIA. I think they might be thrown away now, Sally.

SALLY. I'd think so, too. Been there a week if it's a minute. Some one used to change them every day, but they've seemingly got tired of the job.

VIRGINIA. Yes. Put them away, please.

(SALLY *nods and goes out.*)

MRS. MUNNING (*making the best of it*). I didn't know he'd given it up here altogether.

VIRGINIA. I expect he preferred a proper night's rest, aunt.

MRS. MUNNING. Not he. But that's Paul all over. If he can't get the best he'll have none. Look at the engage-ment ring he gave you.

VIRGINIA. Yes. It's—an engagement ring.

MRS. MUNNING. Ah, but you're like myself, Jenny. You don't value things for their appearance, but for what they mean to you.

VIRGINIA (*doubtfully, fingering the ring*). Yes.

(PAUL *enters, with hat and coat on.*)

PAUL. Good evening.

MRS. MUNNING. Why, you're sooner than I expected.

PAUL. Well, I've settled it. I've done my business. I've got them, mother. How are you, Jenny? (*Comes round and kisses her.*)

MRS. MUNNING. Have you brought them with you, Paul?

PAUL. I'll show you. Let me get my coat off.

MRS. MUNNING. The roses, I mean.

PAUL (*blankly*). Oh, the roses.

MRS. MUNNING (*quickly*). They'll be sending them, I suppose.

PAUL. Well——

VIRGINIA. I'm just going upstairs.

MRS. MUNNING. You needn't run away from him the moment he comes back.

VIRGINIA. No. But I shan't be going out for a walk to-night, aunt. I'll take my hat off. (*Exit* VIRGINIA.)

MRS. MUNNING. Have you no sense at all? Couldn't you tell her the roses were coming?

PAUL. They're not.

MRS. MUNNING. Not coming? And me just telling her they were all you went to Bollington for!

PAUL. You shouldn't tell her lies. You know they weren't all I went for.

MRS. MUNNING. She liked to think they were. You've got a memory like a sieve.

PAUL. I didn't forget. I went to the shop and asked the price. They wanted sixpence each. Sixpence for a single rose. Have you any idea what a lot of roses it takes to make a decent-looking bunch?

MRS. MUNNING. Will you never get it into your thick head that it's worth spending money to gain money?

PAUL. You've got the spending habit lately. There's no need to spend for the sake of spending. I'm engaged to Virginia. What more do you want?

MRS. MUNNING. I want you to keep engaged till you're married. You're growing careless and neglecting her.

PAUL. Neglecting! I gave her a kiss just now.

MRS. MUNNING. That cost you nothing. What made you stop putting flowers in her room?

PAUL. I'm not marrying a wife to run at her heels with

silly flowers. And there isn't a woman on earth worth buying roses for at sixpence a bloom.

MRS. MUNNING. Virginia's five hundred a year's worth it.

PAUL. It's not. Selling flowers at that price is robbery, and I'll be robbed by no one. Look at Joe Wrigley.

MRS. MUNNING. That won't last long.

PAUL. You're right. It won't. Zack will be married on Wednesday and off to Canada on Saturday. Just let Joe Wrigley come here after that. I'll teach him something.

MRS. MUNNING. You've got their tickets?

PAUL (showing them). I told you I had.

MRS. MUNNING. Steerage, I see.

PAUL. Of course they're steerage. Why, do you know we've to give them a matter of ten pounds before they'll let them land?

MRS. MUNNING. Well, we have to start them off with something, Paul.

PAUL. Ten pounds isn't something. It's a thundering lot.

MRS. MUNNING. In a good cause.

PAUL. A good cause is a better cause when it's cheap, and this is coming out a bit expensive.

(*Enter* SALLY.)

MRS. MUNNING. What is it, Sally?

SALLY. The door bell, Mrs. Munning.

(SALLY *crosses and exit.*)

PAUL. An order, if we're lucky.

MRS. MUNNING. Well, you are lucky, lately, aren't you? Everything you can think of 's going right.

(SALLY *re-enters.*)

SALLY. It's Mr. Wrigley and some friends.

(WRIGLEY *enters with* THOMAS MOWATT *and* HARRY SHOE-
BRIDGE. MOWATT *is a fat, red-faced dairyman and* SHOE-
BRIDGE *is a farmer, tall, with brown face and mutton-chop
whiskers.* WRIGLEY *has a large jug of ale and puts it on
table.* (*Exit* SALLY.)

WRIGLEY. Good evening, Mrs. Munning. Come in,
Thomas, Harry. You see, Mrs. Munning, you've been so
amazing good to me lately over a bit of supper at nights
that I thought I'd bring a friend or two this time to test the
vittles.

MRS. MUNNING. You——

WRIGLEY. Ay, and you needn't tire your tongue with
welcoming words. I can read your genial thoughts. And
knowing you hadn't got it here, we brought our own ale
with us. (*Lifting jug.*) It's a real drop of stimulant is
this. Now sit down, Thomas. There you are, Harry.
(*Places chairs.*) Well, now what shall it be ? (*Sits.*) Seeing
we're unexpected like, I think a bit of bread and cheese, eh
Thomas ?

THOMAS. It'll go sweetly with the ale.

WRIGLEY. So it will. Bread and cheese, Mrs. Munning.
I'd not say " no " to biscuits myself.

PAUL (*advancing*). Joe Wrigley——

WRIGLEY. Eh, Paul, I didn't just notice you, but you're
the man we want. We've really come on business, but
we'll get on better when we're fortified with a bite and a sup.
You know what Thomas and Harry are, don't you ?

PAUL (*surrendering*). You'd better get the bread and
cheese out, mother.

(MRS. MUNNING *goes reluctantly and opens door.*)

Mrs. Munning. Sally ! Sally !

(*Exit* Mrs. Munning.)

Wrigley. That's right, Paul. When the Executive Committee of the Little Hulton Savings Club pay a call upon you it's a matter of common sense for you to make them feel at home.

Paul. Mr. Mowatt and Mr. Shoebridge are on the Executive and they're welcome here, but you——

Wrigley. I'm on as well.

Harry. Since last night.

Wrigley. As you say, Harry, since last night. I'm co-opted under rule 17. Cost me a gallon of beer, but I'm co-opted. We're the Executive and we're here on a matter of business concerned with the work of the Society

Paul (*with deference*). What can I do for you, Mr. Shoebridge ?

Harry. Well, I'll tell you, Mr. Munning.

(Mrs. Munning *and* Sally *enter. They put food and glasses on table.* Wrigley *pours ale. They eat and drink during the ensuing. Exit* Sally.)

Harry. You do the catering for our annual picnic, and there's a resolution standing on our minute book, recommend-ing our members to employ you at times of private merry-making. Thank you, Mrs. Munning.

Paul. We've done all catering for your members at contract prices for many years.

Thomas. That's so. And no one likes to break an old connection without warning.

Paul. Break ?

Thomas. I reckon first to last you've made a pretty penny by us.

PAUL. I'm sure our charges to you are moderate, Mr. Mowatt.

THOMAS. They'll do. They'll do—so long as you're giving us what we want.

HARRY. It's not the charges that we're here about exactly.

MRS. MUNNING. Then what is it ?

HARRY. I'm telling you as fast as I can. This is a tasty bit of cheese, Mrs. Munning.

WRIGLEY. Aye. I thought you'd relish it. It's full-flavoured but it doesn't rasp the tongue. It's mellow.

THOMAS. Meller's a great word, Joe. I like things to be meller. I like meller women and meller cheese and meller ale and meller festivals.

HARRY. Did you go to see Mr. Abbott married the other day ?

THOMAS. Did I go ? I'd say so. That was a proper meller occasion.

HARRY. It was that. Mellow right through. He married his wife with port wine, did Mr. Abbott.

THOMAS. I'm not partial to port wine myself. I favour ale at all times and all occasions. Ale's a beverage.

WRIGLEY. And Mr. Abbott's wedding isn't the point to-night.

THOMAS. It was a meller wedding and we want things meller always.

HARRY. That's it in a nutshell, Mr. Munning.

PAUL. I'm sure we make no differences, Mr. Shoebridge.

HARRY. Oh yes, you do. You may not know it, but you do. You have two sorts of catering, and our members want the best, or the Executive will pass a resolution advising all to patronize Wilson's of Norton.

MRS. MUNNING. I hope you won't do that, Mr. Shoe-bridge.

HARRY. Well, if you want to keep our connection, you'll have to do the thing our way.

PAUL. But you don't tell us what your way is. What is it we do wrong?

HARRY. I'm coming to it, lad. I'm going to touch the spot. From what we hear, your Zack's a-wedding Martha Wrigley.

PAUL. Yes?

HARRY. Well, I've nowt against it. Martha's doing unexpected well, but if Zack's satisfied I'm sure I am. But Joe Wrigley tells me that it doesn't stop at that, and being her father he ought to know. You want to emigrate them off to Canada. Now where's the sense in that?

PAUL. It seems best to us.

THOMAS. Well, I think it's rotten.

PAUL. You must allow us to be judges.

MRS. MUNNING. I think that's our business and nobody else's.

WRIGLEY (pushing back chair and rising). Come on, let's be getting over to Wilson's and making our arrangements with him.

THOMAS (rising). Yes, that's the only thing if they're going to talk that road.

PAUL. But I do wish you'd explain. What has Zack's going to Canada to do with it?

HARRY. You want a lot of telling. You have two sorts of jollifications here. Jollifications with Zack Munning and jollifications without. We want them *with*.

MRS. MUNNING. With Zack?

HARRY. He's the difference I've been telling you about.

MRS. MUNNING. Zack is ! He never does anything.

HARRY. He does enough. I know what you mean. He's a bit of a fool at doing most things is Zack, but he's got a gift for jollifications. I couldn't point to where it is myself. Zack's just to come and moon about and drop a word into an ear there and take a woman's arm here and the thing's done. You might call it a knack he has.

THOMAS. He mellers things. That's where it is. It's like this, Mrs. Munning. You can eat cheese without supping ale to it, but you don't get satisfaction. And Paul can run a wedding without Zack being there, but it's not hearty—not¦ what I'd call a jollification. It's stiff and hard. No feeling in it. No mellerness.

HARRY. Zack's got a way with him. He's an artist. If the talk's going flat, or anybody recalls a subject that's not fit to be recalled at a wedding—an old quarrel or such like,—what does Zack do but break a plate ? and smiles that smile of his, and all's well in a moment.

MRS. MUNNING. Well, this is a revelation to me. I don't know what to say.

PAUL. I do. He'll go to Canada.

WRIGLEY. Is that your last word ?

MRS. MUNNING. No. We'll talk this over, Paul.

PAUL. It's gone too far for talking now. I've bought their tickets.

WRIGLEY. They'll do to light a fire with.

MRS. MUNNING. We'll let you have your answer later, Mr. Shoebridge.

HARRY (by door). All right, Mrs. Munning. You're wise enough to know a hasty temper doesn't pay in business. I could give a good guess at your answer.

WRIGLEY. I'm not fond of guessing myself, so I'll stay

here to get it. I'm concerned twice over. As a member of
the Executive and as father of the bride to be.

THOMAS. We'll leave it to you, Joe.

WRIGLEY. I reckon you can.

HARRY. Good evening, Mrs. Munning.

MRS. MUNNING. Good evening to you.

(*Exeunt* THOMAS *and* HARRY.)

MRS. MUNNING. I suppose we can put this down to you,
Joe Wrigley.

WRIGLEY. You might be farther out.

PAUL. You'd nothing to say against emigrating them
when I mentioned it.

WRIGLEY. No, but I thought a lot. I'd a father's feelings,
and they went too deep for words.

MRS. MUNNING. What have you done this for, Joe ?

WRIGLEY. Two reasons, and I don't know which is bigger
of the two. Zack's worth good money here. If I'd a mind
to ruin your trade I'd let him go, and make you find out what
you've missed. But that's not Joseph Wrigley's way. I
kill no geese that lay me golden eggs. And reason number
two. Aye, and this weighs heaviest. I want the pleasure of
knowing they're living in the village here and the satisfaction
of watching your face look sour and sourer for the sight of
them. I'll teach you something for sacking me.

(VIRGINIA *enters, during this speech.*)

PAUL. Will you, Joe ? You've given me two reasons
why you think you will. I'll give you two why you won't.

WRIGLEY. You will ?

MRS. MUNNING. Be careful, Paul. (*She puts hand on his
arm.*)

PAUL (*shaking her off*). The first's Zack isn't married yet to Martha and the second is he isn't going to be. Their engagement's served my purpose.

VIRGINIA. What was your purpose, Paul ?

PAUL. Oh ! I didn't see you, Jenny.

WRIGLEY. Never mind her. You're speaking to me. Zack shall marry Martha or I'll make your name a stink in Little Hulton.

PAUL. Get out.

WRIGLEY. You'll eat a lot of dirt for this, Paul Munning. Banns called and wedding fixed and people asked. (*By door, then turns*). Is Zack to marry Martha ?

PAUL. He's not.

WRIGLEY. Then the band is going to play and, by George, I'll make you dance to it.

(*Exit* WRIGLEY.)

VIRGINIA (*quietly*). You must tell me what this is, Paul.

PAUL. It's Joe Wrigley making a mistake. Thinks he can bounce me, does he ?

MRS. MUNNING. You'd better be careful, Paul. Joe Wrigley's one thing when he's one of our men, but he's another now he's got on that committee.

PAUL. I'd like to wring his neck. The cunning swine.

MRS. MUNNING. Zack's not to go to Canada.

PAUL. All right. He's not. I'll go to Bollington to-morrow and get the money back on the tickets. But he shan't marry Martha either. I'll get even with Joe Wrigley there.

VIRGINIA. What does Zack say ?

PAUL. Zack ? What's Zack to do with it ?

VIRGINIA. It's his marriage, you know.

PAUL. Zack 'll do as he's told. He wasn't marrying her because he wanted to.

VIRGINIA. Why was he marrying?

PAUL. Because I wanted it. I don't want it now.

MRS. MUNNING. We're in a ticklish corner with Joe Wrigley, Paul.

PAUL. Do you want me to hold my hands up to Joe Wrigley?

MRS. MUNNING. You'll take care what you do? I don't want my business damaged worse than it is.

PAUL. *Your* business?

MRS. MUNNING. It is my business, I believe. You're only my manager, and I warn you to be careful or I'll set about making a change. I've learnt something to-night.

VIRGINIA. So have I.

PAUL. Mother, you don't believe Joe's tales of Zack!

MRS. MUNNING. I'd not believe a sacked man's tales of anything, but I believe Mowatt and Shoebridge, and I know who it is they want at the weddings. It's been a shock to me to find they favour Zack, but it's Zack they want and Zack they're going to get.

PAUL. A nice mess he'll make of things.

MRS. MUNNING. That remains to be seen. He's never had his chance till now, but he's just as much my son as you are, Paul.

VIRGINIA. Yes, he was just as much your son when you neglected him and kept him down and gave Paul all your love. And just as much when you and Paul let Zack walk into Wrigley's trap and never raised a hand to save him, and when you schemed to send him out to Canada to save your pride from being hurt, and when you changed your mind about him now—not from regret or any love for Zack,

but when you found your business would do better with him
here. Oh, I've been stupid too. I let myself be blinded
by the dust you both threw in my eyes, but I'm not blinded
now and——

PAUL. Will you be quiet, Virginia ?

MRS. MUNNING. If I made a mistake, Jenny, I've owned
to it.

VIRGINIA. You've owned to it ! Does that make up to
Zack for all the years you've slighted him, for the chances
that he might have had and Paul has robbed him of ?
For——

PAUL. Robbed ! I think you're forgetting whose ring
you're wearing on your finger.

VIRGINIA. Your ring ? Yes. There's your ring.

(*She takes it off and throws it at him. ZACK and MARTHA
enter. MARTHA is in a stupidly elaborate wedding-dress.
The ring misses PAUL, hits ZACK and falls.*)

ZACK. I think I heard something drop.

VIRGINIA. Yes. I've dropped Paul.

MRS. MUNNING. Jenny !

PAUL. You might have damaged that ring badly. It
cost me thirty shillings.

VIRGINIA. You are having an expensive time, lately.

MARTHA (*picking up ring*). Oh, it's a beautiful ring.

PAUL. Yes. Give it to me.

VIRGINIA. No. Put it on, Martha.

PAUL. What !

VIRGINIA. Put it on.

(MARTHA *puts it on.*)

Do you like the look of it on your finger ?

MARTHA It's a vision.

VIRGINIA. Is it ? Do you like the man that goes with that ring ?

PAUL. That's my ring, Virginia.

VIRGINIA. I'm quite aware of that. Do you like Paul, Martha ? Will you take Paul Munning for your lawful wedded husband ?

ZACK. I'm not very quick at thinking, Virginia, but I think you're getting things mixed up like.

PAUL. She's gone mad.

VIRGINIA. Have I aunt ?

MRS. MUNNING. I don't know, Jenny.

VIRGINIA. You do know. You know Joe Wrigley has the power to ruin you unless Martha becomes Mrs. Munning. She's going to become Mrs. Munning, but not Mrs. Zack Munning.

ZACK. But I've passed my word to Martha. We've had banns called in church.

VIRGINIA. Are you in love with Martha, Zack ?

ZACK. Well——

VIRGINIA, Are you or are you not ?

ZACK. You do ask the awkwardest questions, Virginia.

VIRGINIA. That's good enough for me. Martha, it's a pity to waste that wedding-dress. Would you rather marry Zack or Paul ?

MARTHA. I've never dared to lift my eyes as high as Mr. Paul.

VIRGINIA. It's not so high. Stand on a chair if it'll make you feel easier. It's like this, Martha. Paul's missing something by not marrying me, but there's a matter of five hundred pounds that I'll give him in the vestry on his wedding-day with you. Of course if he doesn't marry you there's no five hundred pounds, and there is your father.

MRS. MUNNING. And a new manager for my business too.

PAUL. Mother !

VIRGINIA. So you've got it all three ways, Paul. Martha, you needn't be afraid. Canada with Zack was the riskiest gamble a woman ever thought of, but England with Paul is something solid. You'll have friends to watch you and to watch Paul, too.

PAUL. But—but——

VIRGINIA. That's all right, Paul. You needn't thank me now. And if you'd like to take Martha out for a walk, I shan't prevent you.

MARTHA. Me walk through Little Hulton by the side of Mr. Paul! Oh, Miss Virginia, I'd never have the face.

VIRGINIA. I've told you you're bringing him good money. You give and he takes.

PAUL. Do I take ?

VIRGINIA. Don't you ?

PAUL. Mother, have you nothing to say ?

VIRGINIA. She's come down on the right side of the fence at last, Paul.

MRS. MUNNING. I'll not pretend I'm pleased, but it's a way out.

PAUL. You'd see me sacrificed like this ?

MRS. MUNNING. You'll not forget that Martha's in the room, will you ?

ZACK. I suppose I'll do wrong thing if I open my mouth, but I'll speak my mind for once and chance it.

VIRGINIA. What's the matter, Zack ? You didn't want to marry Martha ?

ZACK. I didn't and I did. I've no right to be selfish, and I didn't like the thought of it at first. I'm the wrong sort of husband for her as I am.

VIRGINIA. Very well, then——

ZACK. Aye. As I am I'm wrong, and I know I'm wrong. But I might not be so wrong in Canada. I've never had a chance afore, and this thing's grown on me a bit. I've wanted my chance, and it looked like I was getting it. You never know what a foreign country will do for a man, and Canada began to look a chance to me. I'd hopes of Canada. And now you say I'm not to marry Martha, and I'll never get a chance again.

MARTHA. I'd rather marry Mr. Paul, if he's willing, Zack.

VIRGINIA. He's willing.

ZACK. Maybe you're right, Martha. Paul's a bigger man than me and I mustn't be selfish. But I'd begun to be hopeful, and I own this is a blow to me. I'll go out for a breath of air.

VIRGINIA. Stay where you are, Zack. Paul and Martha are going out together.

PAUL. That's advertising it a bit, and her in her wedding-gown and all.

VIRGINIA. It's meant to advertise it, Paul. There's your hat. Give her your arm now.

MARTHA. Oh, Mr. Paul !

(*They go up to door, arm in arm.*)

VIRGINIA. And I'll tell you something, Paul. You're great at talking of the cost of things. A pleasant look costs no more than a sour one, so see what you can do.

(*Exeunt* PAUL *and* MARTHA. VIRGINIA *closes door.*)

Now then, aunt, is there anything you'd like to say to Zack ?

MRS. MUNNING. He's the cause of more trouble than he's worth, and has been since the day he was born.

ZACK. Yes, mother. I knew it must be all my fault some road.

VIRGINIA. I suppose that way of speaking to him is force of habit, aunt. But it's time you changed your habits now. Don't you think you'd feel better if you apologized to Zack ?

MRS. MUNNING. Apologized !

VIRGINIA. I've a belief myself in paying debts.

MRS. MUNNING. I don't owe Zack for much.

VIRGINIA. Only thirty years' neglect.

ZACK. You mustn't talk like that to mother, Jenny. You can't expect a great soft thing like me to get same care taken of him as she took of Paul. You don't treat cart-horses like you'd treat a racer.

VIRGINIA (to MRS. MUNNING, ignoring ZACK). So you've nothing to say to him ?

MRS. MUNNING. I don't know that I have.

VIRGINIA. You're leaving quite a lot to me.

MRS. MUNNING. We know what's good for Zack. Some folk don't pay for kindness.

VIRGINIA. Some never get a chance. Zack's had your method long enough. We'll try mine now.

MRS. MUNNING. And what is yours ?

VIRGINIA. Bring me some hot water and a towel, Zack.

ZACK. Hot water ?

VIRGINIA. In a jug.

ZACK. Yes, Jenny. I knew there'd be hot water in it somewhere. (Exit ZACK.)

MRS. MUNNING. What's this for ?

VIRGINIA. A clean start and a clean chin and Zack's first lesson in the art of self-respect.

MRS. MUNNING. Meaning you're going to swell his head.

VIRGINIA. No, aunt. Only to shave his beard. I'm

going to talk to Zack and a lather-brush will be a handy
thing to stop his mouth with if he tries to answer back before
I've done.

(ZACK *re-enters with steaming jug and a towel.*)

ZACK. It's very hot. I found the kettle on the boil.

VIRGINIA. All the better.

ZACK (*apprehensively*). Yes, Jenny.

MRS. MUNNING. And you think I'll stay here and watch
you do it ?

VIRGINIA. Well, aunt, I rather hoped you wouldn't.

MRS. MUNNING. You're taking charge of things, young
lady.

VIRGINIA. I've come to the conclusion that it's time.

(MRS. MUNNING *meets her eye, quails and goes out.*)

Zack, go upstairs and bring me down the birthday present
that I gave you.

ZACK. It's not upstairs, Jenny.

VIRGINIA. Where is it, then ? I want it.

ZACK. I keep it in my pocket.

VIRGINIA. No wonder your coat fits like a sack. Give it
me.

ZACK. You're not going to take it off me because I didn't
use it, are you ?

VIRGINIA. I'm going to use it. Sit down. (*She pushes
him into chair and puts towel round his neck.*) Tell me why
you carried this about with you.

ZACK. It's because I——(*hesitates.*)

VIRGINIA. Well ?

ZACK. Because you gave it me.

VIRGINIA. I gave it you for use. Keep still now. (*She
trims his beard with scissors.*)

ZACK. Yes, Jenny. I know, but I couldn't bring myself to do it. They're too grand for using on the likes of me. Oh ! (*She deliberately pricks him.*)

VIRGINIA. What is it ?

ZACK. You ran the scissors into me. It doesn't matter though.

(*She pricks again.*)

Oh, Jenny, that did hurt a bit.

VIRGINIA. I meant it to. Don't you dare to say it doesn't matter when you're hurt or I'll hurt you again.

ZACK. No, Jenny.

(*She turns to table and makes lather.*)

VIRGINIA. And when I give you anything and tell you to use it, you won't imagine it's too grand for you. You'll use it. (*Her back is still turned to him. He fingers the stubble on his chin and nervously holds the chair-arms, watching her timorously.*)

ZACK. Yes, Jenny.

VIRGINIA (*turning with lather-brush*). Very well. Now I can start talking to you. (*She holds brush poised. He eyes it.*)

ZACK. You've not done badly up to now for a non-starter. (*She puts brush in his mouth*). Oof !

VIRGINIA (*lathering*). If you open your mouth again unless I tell you to, that's what you'll get. Now, Zack Munning, who do you think you are ? (*Stands from him*). You may answer.

ZACK. Well I suppose I'm——I dunno. I'm nobody much.

VIRGINIA (*approaching and lathering*). You can't answer. Then I'll tell you. You are not nobody. You're a person

of considerable importance. For one thing, you're the
mainstay of your mother's business. When you go to
weddings, they're liked, and when you don't they're disliked.
Paul is not popular. You are. You may speak.

ZACK. You've no right to run down Paul like that, Jenny.

VIRGINIA. I'm not running him down. I'm putting
him in his place in comparison with you. Now, is that
understood ? You're of more value here than he is.

ZACK. Oh, but, Jenny—oof ! (*He gets the brush in his
mouth.*)

VIRGINIA. If you like a mouthful of soap at every word
I utter you can have it. If you don't, sit quiet and listen.
Where was I coming to ? Oh yes. Martha Wrigley. You
didn't love her, Zack. Why did you let them force her on
to you ?

ZACK. I do hate argument, Jenny. Paul argued and
Joe argued and he's a powerful voice for arguing has Joe, and
so I just said " yes " to make an end of it.

VIRGINIA (*taking razor*). You'd better turn round to the
light now. I don't want to plough your face. Carry the
chair to the window.

ZACK. Yes, Jenny.

VIRGINIA. Sit down and let me see what I can make of
you. (*She shaves.*) You just said " Yes " to save yourself
the trouble of saying " No " and never thought of anybody
else but Paul and Joe.

ZACK (*moving in protest*). Oh yes, I did, Jenny.

VIRGINIA (*alarmed*). Be careful, Zack. I don't want to
cut you.

ZACK. Well, I did think of some one else.

VIRGINIA. Who ?

ZACK. I thought of Martha.

VIRGINIA. Never mind Martha.

ZACK. But I must mind her. She looked to me for consolation did Martha, and I don't think Paul's as good at consoling a wench as I am.

VIRGINIA. Oh ? So we've found something we're better at than he is, have we ?

ZACK. I'm bound to think of Martha's feelings, Jenny.

VIRGINIA. Martha's parading the high street with Paul. Her feelings are all right.

ZACK. My conscience isn't easy about her, Jenny. We've been called in church together and——

VIRGINIA (*holding out razor*). And you can finish shaving by yourself.

ZACK. But I don't know how. I've never used a razor in my life.

(VIRGINIA *puts razor on table.* ZACK *rises, half shaved.*)

VIRGINIA. It's time you learned.

ZACK. You were getting on so well.

VIRGINIA. So were you till you began to talk rubbish about Martha Wrigley. Go and ask her to finish shaving you.

ZACK. Have I said anything to offend you, Jenny ?

VIRGINIA. Have you said—— ? You think a lot about other people, Zack. Do you never think of me ?

ZACK. I do that. But it's not the same.

VIRGINIA. The same as what ?

ZACK. It's common thinking when I think of them. When I think of you it's something a bit special. It's thinking with my hat off, like going into church. It's Sunday best and I couldn't bring myself to talk of it the same way as I'd talk of them. It's not for talking of at all. It's holy-like. That's why I haven't mentioned it.

VIRGINIA (*takes up razor*. ZACK *flinches*). Sit down again. I'll finish shaving you.

ZACK. Will you, Jenny ? (*He sits.*)

VIRGINIA. Yes. Don't talk or you'll get cut. Now listen, Zack. Martha Wrigley's getting what she wants. She's marrying Paul and she'll be the proudest woman in the place. So you can put her out of mind. If you want to say " good-bye " to her, you can go and say it when I've finished shaving you. Only you'll say it in words. You're a bit too free with your consolations, and I've not shaved you for Martha Wrigley to have the benefit of your virgin chin. You've finished with her, Zack, you understand ?

ZACK. Yes, Jenny.

VIRGINIA. Very well. Now you can get up and look at yourself in that glass.

ZACK (*peering into glass in lid of shaving set*). Why, Jenny, I'd not have known myself. Is yon lad me ?

VIRGINIA. It's you.

ZACK. Well, I tell you what, Jenny, if I'd met that face in the lane on anybody else but me, I'd have said he wasn't a bad looking chap at all.

VIRGINIA. It's not a face you're meeting in the lane. It's your face.

ZACK. That's the surprising part about it. Why, it's very near worth taking the trouble to shave every day.

VIRGINIA. I'll see you take the trouble.

ZACK. And I'll look like this every day !

VIRGINIA. You will.

ZACK. Well, but if that's so, and I'm free of Martha, why. . . . No. I'm getting ahead too fast.

VIRGINIA. Not you. Take another look at yourself if you're afraid about anything.

ZACK (*looking*). I'm pretty near good-looking enough to chance it. Dang it, I will chance it, and all—No. No. I'm not quite bold enough for that.

VIRGINIA (*holding glass in front of him*). Look again.

ZACK. Well, you can't eat me anyhow. Jenny, I've got a heap of love for you. I've loved you since the day I met you, and I've been the miserablest chap on earth because of what's been happening since. Things always do go wrong with me, and they've been going the wrongest road they could, but, by gum, there's just a chance to put them right this time, and I'll dash at it if I'm hanged for it. Jenny it's the most bowdacious thing to come from me to you, but I'm wrought up to point and I've got to speak or bust. Will you have me, lass ?

VIRGINIA. Kiss me, Zack.

ZACK. But—but—do you mean to say you'll——

VIRGINIA. You great baby.

ZACK (*embracing her*). Eh, I could hug you till you broke. Love ? Love's the finest state of man. I'm—I'm——No. There aren't words made for this. Its too tremendous big for words. Jenny, it's true ? You're not—You're not just playing with me.

VIRGINIA. No. It's true. Oh, Zack !

ZACK. Jenny ! (*Kiss.*)

CURTAIN.

Lightning Source UK Ltd.
Milton Keynes UK
UKOW06f1320210515

252004UK00013B/197/P